KT-176-764
advancing learning, changing lives

Numeracy

Level 1

LEARNING CENTRE

CLASS NO: 510.1 ROB

ACC NO: 066730

Harrow College
Harrow Weald Campus, Learning Centre
Brookshill, Harrow Weald, Middx.
HA3 6RR   0208 909 6248

A PEARSON COMPANY

Carol Roberts

Consultant Joh

HARROW COLLEGE

066730

About this book

This book has been written to support you in taking the Adult Numeracy Level 1 test. The authors are experienced teachers and examiners who know the sorts of questions that are usually asked in the test.

How to use the book

The book is arranged into sections which cover the Adult Numeracy Level 1 criteria. Each section starts with a list of what you should already know and what you will learn. Use this list to check your progress.

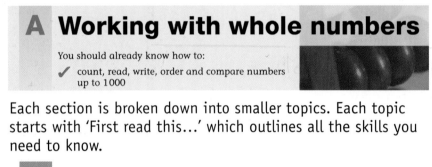

A Working with whole numbers

You should already know how to:
✓ count, read, write, order and compare numbers up to 1000

Each section is broken down into smaller topics. Each topic starts with 'First read this...' which outlines all the skills you need to know.

1 Reading and writing whole numbers

First read this ...

▷ Every digit in a number has a value, depending on its position in the number. This is called its **place value**.

Remember
The individual figures in a

The 'Now try it!' heading starts off the exercise, giving you plenty of practice at the key techniques. The questions are mainly set in context as in the actual test, so that you get relevant practice throughout.

Now try it!

1. Round these numbers to the nearest ten.
   a 124 _____ b 349 _____ c 3985 _____

 The CD icon in the margin points you to additional learning material on the free Hot Topics CD-ROM included with this book.

At the end of each section, to help you remember what you have learned, 'First complete this...' repeats the important information from the section, leaving out key words. Try to fill in the words then look back through the section to check you are correct.

First complete this ...

▷ Every digit in a number has a value, depending on its position in the number. This is called its _____ _____ .

The final 'Now try it!' of the section consists of practice test questions in multiple-choice format so you can practise for the real thing.

Contents

A Working with whole numbers

You should already know how to:

✓ count, read, write, order and compare numbers up to 1000

✓ add and subtract whole numbers with up to three digits

✓ multiply and divide two-digit numbers by single-digit numbers

✓ approximate by rounding.

By the end of this section you will know how to:

▷ recognise large numbers and calculate with them using different methods

▷ round numbers to the nearest 10, 100 or 1000

▷ work out whether to add, subtract, multiply or divide in word problems

▷ check answers using the inverse operation

▷ handle negative numbers in context.

1 Reading and writing whole numbers

First read this ...

▷ Every digit in a number has a value, depending on its position in the number. This is called its **place value**.

You can use a **place-value table** to work out the value of each digit in a whole number. Write the digits, beginning from the right.

> **Remember**
>
> The individual figures in a number are called **numerals** or **digits**.

Example 1: Write the number 87 529 in words.

First, put the number in a place-value table.

M	H Th	T Th	Th	H	T	U
millions	hundred thousands	ten thousands	thousands	hundreds	tens	units
		8	7	5	2	9

The number 87 529 has 8 ten thousands, 7 thousands, 5 hundreds, 2 tens and 9 units.

Answer: eighty-seven thousand, five hundred and twenty-nine

When you write a cheque you have to write an amount in words and figures.

Example 2: Write the number five million, one hundred and two thousand and forty-five in figures.

Draw a place-value table and fill in the digits, from the right.

M	H Th	T Th	Th	H	T	U
5	1	0	2	0	4	5

Answer: 5 102 045

> **Tip**
>
> Write 0 in the columns to show there are no ten thousands and no hundreds.

▶▶ *Now try it!*

1. Ring the correct way of writing each number in words.

 a 4 322

   A Forty-three thousand and twenty-two

   B Four thousand, three hundred and twenty-two

 b 16 308

   A Sixteen thousand, three hundred and eight

   B One hundred and sixty-three thousand and eight

 c 816 395

   A Eight million, sixteen thousand, three hundred and ninety-five

   B Eight hundred and sixteen thousand, three hundred and ninety-five

 d 1 455 372

   A One million, four hundred and fifty-five thousand, three hundred and seventy-two

   B One hundred and four million, fifty-five thousand, three hundred and seventy-two

2. The population of a town was worked out to be twenty-three thousand, four hundred and thirty. Write this number in figures.

   _____

3. Five hundred and sixty-six thousand, two hundred and fifteen people visited a museum over the holiday period. What is this number in figures?

   _____

4. In one year, a shop sold two million, four hundred and twenty thousand, seven hundred and two music CDs. Write this number in figures.

   _____

2 Rounding

You can round numbers to the nearest 10, 100 or 1 000.

The value of the **key digit** tells you whether to round the number up or down:

▷ The key digit is immediately to the right of the place value you are rounding to.

  ▷ Round **up** when the key digit is 5, 6, 7, 8 or 9.

  ▷ Round **down** when the key digit is 1, 2, 3 or 4.

If you are rounding to the nearest *ten*, then the key digit is the *units* digit.

Example 1: Round 3 457 to the nearest ten.

The key digit is to the right of the tens digit: 3 45<u>7</u>

The key digit, 7, is **more than 5** so **round up**, from 57 to 60.

Answer: 3 460

If you are rounding to the nearest hundred, then the key digit is the tens digit.

Example 2: Round 3 457 to the nearest hundred.

The key digit is the tens digit: 3 4<u>5</u>7

The key digit is 5 so **round up**, from 457 to 500.

Answer: 3 500

If you are rounding to the nearest thousand, then the key digit is the hundreds digit.

Example 3: Round 3 457 to the nearest thousand.

The key digit is the hundreds digit: 3 <u>4</u>57

As 4 is less than 5, **round down**, from 3 457 to 3 000.

Answer: 3 000

> **Tip**
>
> A number line can help you decide whether to round up or down.
>
>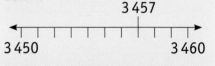
>
> 3 457 is closer to 3 460 than 3 450, so **round up**.

> **Tip**
>
> The hundreds digit is to the right of the thousands digit.

Now try it!

1. Round these numbers to the nearest ten.

   a 124 _____   b 349 _____   c 3 985 _____

2. How many miles are shown on this car's mileometer, to the nearest ten miles?

_____

3. Ring the number which is 725 rounded to the nearest ten:

   a 700   b 720   c 730

4. Ring the number which is 8 307 rounded to the nearest ten:

   a 8 000   b 8 300   c 8 310

5. Round each of these numbers to the nearest hundred.

   a 3 885 _____   b 1 946 _____   c 12 011 _____

6. A bricklayer needs 14 675 bricks for a job. What is this number to the nearest hundred?

   _____

7. Ring the number which is 4 356 rounded to the nearest 100:

   a 4 300   b 4 350   c 4 400

8. Ring the number which is 69 049 rounded to the nearest 100:

   a 69 000   b 69 050   c 69 100

9. Round each of these numbers to the nearest thousand.

   a 1 500 _____   b 13 499 _____

10. Round each of these numbers to the nearest thousand.

   a 3 357 _____   b 45 601 _____   c 21 075 _____

11. A woman earns £23 498 per year. How much is this, to the nearest thousand pounds?

   _____

12. Ring the number which is 1 995 rounded to the nearest thousand:

   a 1 000   b 1 900   c 2 000

13. Ring the number which is 33 744 rounded to the nearest thousand:

   a 30 000   b 33 000   c 34 000

3 Adding whole numbers

First read this ...

Here are two different ways of adding numbers.

■ The traditional, column method

■ The partitioning method.

The two methods give the same answer.

The traditional way to add numbers is to write them in a column, with digits of the same place value aligned. You add each column of digits, starting from the right.

Tip

The important thing is to choose a method you like and can use to get the correct answer.

Example 1: Work out 78 967 + 7 827

Align the place values:

Work right to left:

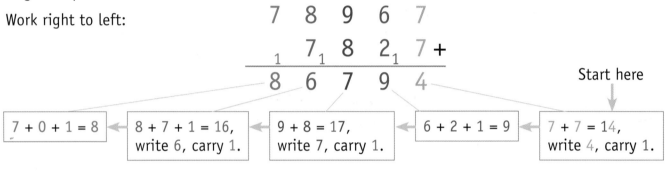

Answer: 86 794

The **partitioning method** breaks the numbers up into parts that have the same place value. You then add these parts.

Example 2: Work out 78 967 + 7 827

78 967 + 7 827

Units: 7 + 7 =	14
Tens: 60 + 20 =	80
Hundreds: 900 + 800 =	1 700
Thousands: 8000 + 7000 =	15 000
Tens of thousands: 70 000 + 0 =	70 000

Answer: 86 794

Now try it!

Use your preferred method to add the following numbers.

1. 13 236 + 2 592

2. a 3708 + 29142   b 50019 + 102

_____   _____

Tip

Use a place-value table to help you align the digits for the partitioning method.

3. 12789 + 18521

_____

4. a 2067 + 34120   b 21997 + 10985

_____   _____

5. 869 + 1037 + 43454

_____

6. A band played for two nights in the same town. The audience figures for the two nights were 5879 and 4233. How many people saw the band?

_____

7. In three rounds of a computer game a boy scored 2346 points, 4559 points and 3008 points. How many points did he score in total?

_____

Test tip

Addition questions usually use the words **total** or **altogether**.

8. At two semi-final football matches, the attendances were 34236 and 19474. How many attended the two matches in total?

_____

9. A woman has £2403 in one savings account, £1295 in another and £560 in a third. How much has she saved altogether?

_____

10. Ring the method you prefer.

    traditional method   partitioning method

4 Subtracting whole numbers

First read this ...

Here are two methods for subtracting numbers.

- The traditional, column method

- Counting on in jumps.

In the **traditional method** you write the bigger number above the smaller number, lining up digits with the same place values. Then subtract the digits in each column, starting from the right.

Example 1: Work out 2 373 – 676

Write the numbers in place-value columns. Subtract each column, starting from the right.

Tip

Choose a method you like and can use to get the correct answer.

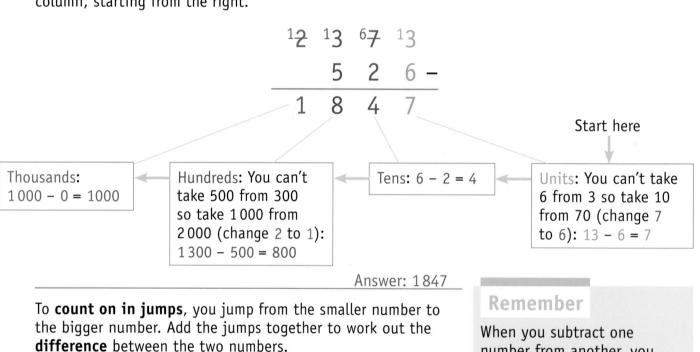

$$
\begin{array}{cccc}
{}^{1}2 & {}^{1}3 & {}^{6}\!\!7 & {}^{1}3 \\
 & 5 & 2 & 6 \\
\hline
1 & 8 & 4 & 7
\end{array}
$$

Start here

| Thousands: 1 000 – 0 = 1000 | Hundreds: You can't take 500 from 300 so take 1 000 from 2 000 (change 2 to 1): 1 300 – 500 = 800 | Tens: 6 – 2 = 4 | Units: You can't take 6 from 3 so take 10 from 70 (change 7 to 6): 13 – 6 = 7 |

Answer: 1847

To **count on in jumps**, you jump from the smaller number to the bigger number. Add the jumps together to work out the **difference** between the two numbers.

Example 2: Work out 2 373 – 526

The number line below shows how to work out the jumps.

Remember

When you subtract one number from another, you are **finding the difference** between them.

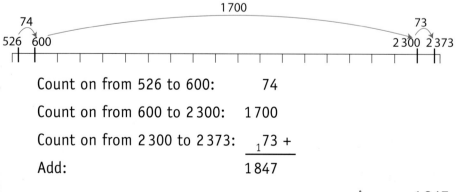

Count on from 526 to 600:   74

Count on from 600 to 2 300:   1 700

Count on from 2 300 to 2 373:   ₁73 +

Add: 1 847

Answer: 1847

Remember

Use your chosen method to add the numbers.

▶▶ *Now try it!*

Use your preferred method to find the answers.

1. 13 436 − 7 392

Test tip

Check your answer makes sense. 13 436 − 7 392 is about 13 000 − 7 000 = 6 000.

_____

2. a 25 355 − 18 261   b 72 300 − 41 856

_____   _____

3. a 16 478 − 8 169   b 63 444 − 37 088

_____   _____

4. a 8 569 − 1 088   b 47 473 − 26 895

_____   _____

5. a 6 500 − 3 421   b 29 115 − 3 206

_____   _____

6. a 27 455 − 18 637   b 80 326 − 79 488

_____   _____

7. Ring the method you prefer.

   traditional method   counting on method

5 Multiplying whole numbers

First read this ...

You can multiply numbers in any order.

Example 1: Work out 3 × 5 × 12

Here are two different ways.

1 First work out 3 × 5 = 15.   **2** First work out 5 × 12 = 60.

Then work out 15 × 12 = 180. Then work out 3 × 60 = 180.

Answer: 180

The second way is probably the easiest, because the second multiplication, 3 × 60, is easier than 15 × 12.

▷ When you **multiply** a number by **10**, all the digits in the number move **one place to the left**.

Example 2: Work out 86 × 10

H	T	U	
	8	6	× 10
8	6	0	

So, 86 × 10 = 860

Answer: 860

20 = 2 × 10. To multiply by 20, multiply by 2 first, then multiply by 10.

Example 3: Work out 25 × 20

25 × 20 = 25 × 2 × 10 = 50 × 10 = 500

Answer: 500

▷ When you **multiply** a number by **100**, all the digits in the number move **two places to the left**.

▷ When you **multiply** a number by **1000**, all the digits in the number move **three places to the left**.

Example 4: Work out **a** 86 × 100 **b** 86 × 1000

	Th	H	T	U	
			8	6	
		8	6	0	× 10
	8	6	0	0	× 10
8	6	0	0	0	× 10

a 86 × 100 = 8 600
Answer: 8 600
b 86 × 1 000 = 86 000
Answer: 86 000

Tip

Look for combinations of numbers that are easy to multiply.

Remember

100 = 10 × 10
1 000 = 10 × 10 × 10
Use these to break down the calculation.

▶▶ *Now try it!*

1. a Work out 8 × 6 × 5 _____

    b School meals cost £3.00 a day. How much will it cost a
       student to have school meals for four weeks?

       _____

2. Work out:
    a 23 × 10 =   b 890 × 10 =   c 10 × 64 =

       _____   _____   _____

3. Photocopier paper costs £8 per box. How much do ten
    boxes cost?

    _____

4. Work out:
    a 21 × 40 =   b 47 × 20 =   c 122 × 30 =

       _____   _____   _____

> **Tip**
>
> 20 = 2 × 10
> 30 = 3 × 10
> 40 = 4 × 10

5. Potatoes cost 72 pence per kilogram. A cook buys a 50 kg
    sack of potatoes. How much does he have to pay?

    _____

6. Work out:
    a 3 × 100 =   b 15 × 100 =   c 100 × 26 =

       _____   _____   _____

7. Fifteen friends each put in £100 to buy a birthday present.
    How much can they spend on the present?

    _____

8. Work out:
    a 35 × 200 =   b 56 × 300 =   c 400 × 14 =

       _____   _____   _____

> **Tip**
>
> 200 = 2 × 100
> 300 = 3 × 100
> 400 = 4 × 100

9. Twenty charity workers each raise £200. How much do they
    raise in total?

    _____

10. Work out:
    a 24 × 1 000 =   b 60 × 1 000 =   c 1 000 × 302 =

       _____   _____   _____

11. A woman earns £2 000 per month as a part-time store
    manager. How much does she earn in one year?

    _____

> **Test tip**
>
> Don't forget to include units
> (for money or measurements)
> in your answers.

12. Work out:
    a 13 × 2 000 =   b 12 × 5 000 =   c 108 × 3 000 =

       _____   _____   _____

First read this ...

Here are two different ways of multiplying numbers.

The traditional, column method
Write each number, one below another, with digits of the same place value lined up, and use long multiplication.

Example 1: Work out 48 × 32

Write 48 and 32 in the grid. Line up the units.

		4	8	
		3	2	×
		9^1	6	
1	$_1$4^2	4	0	+
1	5	3	6	

Multiply by 2 first:
8 × 2 = 16, write 6, carry 1
4 × 2 = 8, 8 + 1 = 9

Multiply by 30:
write 0 in the units column
3 × 8 = 24, write 4, carry 2
3 × 4 = 12, 12 + 2 = 14

Adding: 96 + 1 440 = 1 536

Answer: 1 536

The grid method
Use place value to break or partition each number in the multiplication into different parts.

Example 2: 48 × 32

Partition each number:
48 = 40 + 8
32 = 30 + 2

×	40	8
30	1 200	240
2	80	16

1 200 +
240 +
80 +
16

Answer: 1 536

> **Tip**
> Choose a method you like and can use to get the correct answer.

> **Tip**
> Write the different parts carefully in the grid so that the correct parts are multiplied together.

▶▶ *Now try it!*

1. a 46 × 35 =   b 23 × 19 =   c 84 × 67 =

    _____   _____   _____

2. Twenty-seven friends each pay £25 for a day-trip on a boat. How much do they pay in total?

    _____

3. Two hundred and fifty people each buy a £15 ticket for a concert. How much was raised from ticket sales?

    _____

4. a 64 × 27 =   b 58 × 45 =   c 85 × 36 =

    _____   _____   _____

5. On average, 275 people attend a local swimming pool every week. How many people go swimming in a year?

    Tip

    52 weeks = 1 year.

    _____

6. A company employs 55 security guards. Each guard earns £7 an hour and works for 5 hours per day. How much does the company pay in total per day?

    _____

7 Dividing whole numbers

First read this ...

You should know how to divide by small numbers.

Example 1: Work out $60 \div 4$

$60 \div 4$ can be written as: $4\overline{)6\,{}^2 0}$ with $1\,5$ above

$6 \div 4 = 1$ with remainder 2, write 1 above the line, over the 6, carry the 2.

$20 \div 4 = 5$, write 5 above the line, over the 0.

Answer: 15

▷ When you **divide** a number by **10**, all the digits in the number move **one place to the right**.

> **Tip**
>
> Division is the **opposite** of multiplication, so the **opposite rules** apply.

Example 2: $250 \div 10$

All the digits move one place to the right.

H	T	U
2	5	0
	2	5

$\div 10$

Answer: 25

▷ When you **divide** a whole number by **100**, all the digits in the number move **two places to the right**.

Example 3: $4\,800 \div 100$

All the digits move two places to the right.

Th	H	T	U
4	8	0	0
	4	8	0
		4	8

$\div 10$
$\div 10$
$\div 100$

Answer: 48

$20 = 2 \times 10$. To divide by 20, divide by 10 then divide by 2.

Example 4: $240 \div 20$

Divide the number by 10 first, then divide the result by 2.

$240 \div 20 = 240 \div 10 \div 2$
$\qquad\qquad = 24 \div 2 = 12$

Answer: 12

▶▶ *Now try it!*

Work out these divisions:

1. a 24 ÷ 8 = _____   b 36 ÷ 4 = _____

   c 7)63   d 9)72

2. a What is twenty-five divided by five?

   _____

   b Share £45 equally among five people.

   _____

   c Split £72 into six equal shares.

   _____

Test tip

A question that includes **shares** or **sharing** usually means you need to **divide**.

3. a 200 ÷ 10   b 1 560 ÷ 10   c 2 030 ÷ 10

   _____   _____   _____

4. a 230 ÷ 10   b 4 050 ÷ 10   c 600 ÷ 10

   _____   _____   _____

5. a 1 300 ÷ 100   b 24 600 ÷ 100   c 30 500 ÷ 100

   _____   _____   _____

6. Circle the correct answer.

   a 75 300 ÷ 100 =   A 753   B 7 503   C 7 530

   b 120 400 ÷ 100 = A 1 204   B 2 040   C 1 240

7. a 360 ÷ 30   b 2 700 ÷ 90   c 5 400 ÷ 20

   _____   _____   _____

Tip

30 = 3 x 10
50 = 5 x 10
80 = 8 x 10
90 = 9 x 10

8. Circle the correct answer.

   a 450 ÷ 50 =   A 9   B 90

   b 6 400 ÷ 80 =   A 8   B 80   C 800

9. a 1 500 ÷ 300   b 4 800 ÷ 400   c 56 000 ÷ 800

   _____   _____   _____

10. Circle the correct answer.

    a 35 000 ÷ 500 = A 70   B 700   C 7 000

    b 28 000 ÷ 200 = A 14   B 140   C 1 400

8 Division with larger numbers

First read this ...

Here are two useful methods for dividing by bigger numbers:

- ■ The traditional method
- ■ Repeated subtraction.

The **traditional method** is similar to short division.

Tip

Choose the method you prefer and that gives you the right answer.

Example 1: Work out 672 ÷ 12

Set it out as a normal short division.

```
      5 6
12) 6 7 ⁷2
```

Or set it out as long division like this.

Tip

This short method of division can be difficult if you don't know your tables very well.

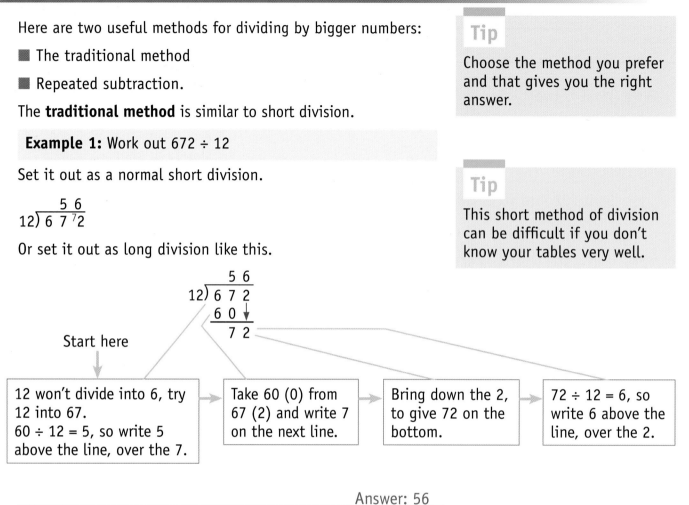

```
      5 6
12) 6 7 2
    6 0 ↓
      7 2
```

Start here

| 12 won't divide into 6, try 12 into 67. 60 ÷ 12 = 5, so write 5 above the line, over the 7. | Take 60 (0) from 67 (2) and write 7 on the next line. | Bring down the 2, to give 72 on the bottom. | 72 ÷ 12 = 6, so write 6 above the line, over the 2. |

Answer: 56

In the **repeated subtraction** method, you break the division into smaller steps, by subtracting until there is nothing left.

Example 2: 672 ÷ 12

```
12) 6 7 2
    6 0 0  = 50 × 12
      7 2
      6 0  =   5 × 12
      1 2
      1 2  =   1 × 12
        0    56 × 12
```

Subtract the highest multiple below 672 (600). 672 − 600 = 72.

Subtract the highest multiple below 72 (60). 72 − 60 = 12.

Subtract 12: 12 − 12 = 0.

Answer: 56

Tip

Draw up a table of multiples:

2 × 12 =	24
5 × 12 =	60
10 × 12 =	120
20 × 12 =	240
50 × 12 =	600
100 × 12 =	1 200

Remember

Multiples are the answers in the times tables.

▶▶ *Now try it!*

1. Use your preferred method to work out these divisions.

    a 234 ÷ 13

    b 517 ÷ 11

Test tip
There are different ways of dividing with larger numbers. It is important to choose a method that you like and can use to get the correct answer.

    13) 2 3 4

    11) 5 1 7

    c 322 ÷ 14

    d 255 ÷ 15

    14) 3 2 2

    15) 2 5 5

    e 405 ÷ 15

    f 875 ÷ 25

    15) 4 0 5

    25) 8 7 5

    g 592 ÷ 16

    h 1512 ÷ 24

    16) 5 9 2

    24) 1 5 1 2

9 Solving word problems

First read this …

When given word problems to solve:

■ Find the important information so you can write the correct calculation

■ Decide whether to add, subtract, multiply or divide.

> **Example:** At a football match there were 15 687 'home' fans and 8 622 'away' fans. How many fans were at the match altogether?

Write the calculation, using numbers and the correct symbols.

$$15\,687 + 8\,622 = \begin{array}{r} {}^{1}1{}^{1}5\ {}^{1}6\,8\,7 \\ 8\ 6\,2\,2\ + \\ \hline 2\,4\ 3\,0\,9 \end{array}$$

Answer: 24 309

Test tip

Always read the problem very carefully.

Tip

Altogether usually tells you to **add** the numbers.

Now try it!

1. A boy has saved £237 and wants to spend some of his money. He wants to leave £195 in his account. How much can he take out?

2. In 2002, a bookstore sold 34 236 books. The store aims to sell 19 474 more in 2005. What is the bookstore's target for 2005?

3. A car has done 33 778 miles. It needs to be serviced when it has done 46 000 miles. How many more miles can it do before it is serviced?

4. A girl has £473 in a bank account. She pays in £46. Then she writes out one cheque for £289 and another for £67. How much is in the account after each transaction?

Test tip

■ **Take** often means **subtract**.

■ **More** usually means you need to **add**.

■ **How many more** or **how much more** usually tells you to **subtract**.

Tip

Break the problem down into separate addition and subtraction calculations.

5. A woman takes out a loan and agrees to pay back £85 per month for 36 months. How much will she pay back in total?

_____

Tip

In this problem, **per month** and **in total** are clues that tell you to **multiply**.

6. A gym charges £49 per month for membership. What will be the total cost of membership for one year?

_____

Test tip

Look for a clue in the answer. The answer to 49 × 12 must end in 8 because 2 × 9 = 18.

7. a A secretary needs to save £595 to pay for a holiday. He can save £35 per week. How many weeks will it take him to save the money he needs?

_____

b Twenty-four friends split the hire of a party hall equally. The hire cost comes to £840. How much does each person pay?

_____

8. A householder pays £384 for electricity in a year. She pays in twelve equal monthly instalments. How much does she pay each month?

_____

9. A grocer's profit for one year is £230 222. One year later it is £235 749. How much more profit did he make in the second year?

_____

10. A computer expert earns £480 for working 12 hours every weekend. How much does she earn per hour?

_____

Harrow College
Harrow Weald Campus, Learning Centre
Brookshill, Harrow Weald, Middx.
HA3 6RR   0208 909 6248

First read this ...

To check an answer, do an **inverse** or opposite operation. This means doing a calculation backwards.

Remember

The opposite of an operation is its **inverse operation**.

▷ Add and subtract are opposite operations.

Example 1: Check that 425 − 36 = 389 is correct.

Start with the answer: 389.

Do the opposite of the calculation.

You took away 36 so, to check, you add 36: 389 + 36.

When you do the addition, you get: 389 + 36 = 425.

425 is the number you started with.

Answer: The calculation is correct.

▷ Multiply and divide are opposite operations.

Example 2: A girl earns £6 per hour. In one week she works 18 hours and expects to be paid £108. How can she check that she has calculated the correct amount?

She worked out £6 × 18 = £108.

Check this by working backwards, and using division.

$$\begin{array}{r} 1\,8 \\ 6\overline{)1\,0\,{}^{4}8} \end{array}$$

Answer: 108 ÷ 6 = 18

Test Tip

Always check your calculations in the test.

You can use quick calculations or **estimates**, using numbers that have been rounded up or down, to see if an answer is 'about right'.

Example 3: Is the answer to 2 104 × 19 = 21 080 correct?

Check by rounding the numbers to the nearest ten.

2 104 rounded to the nearest ten is 2 100.

19 rounded to the nearest ten is 20.

2 100 × 20 = 42 000

The answer of 21 080 is nowhere near the estimated answer of 42 000.

Answer: No.

▶▶ *Now try it!*

Use inverse operations to check these answers.

1. a 256 + 462 = 718   b 343 − 219 = 124

   _____   _____

   c 4 133 + 2 167 = 6 300   d 2 577 − 1 568 = 1 008

   _____   _____

2. a 15 × 48 = 720   b 672 ÷ 21 = 32

   _____   _____

   c 25 × 25 = 650   d 3 312 ÷ 24 = 138

   _____   _____

3. A pilot has flown 276 000 miles in one year. He flies the same number of miles every month. He calculates the monthly distance to be 23 000 miles. Is he correct?

   _____

4. A boy has £479 in his bank account. He writes a cheque for £150 and pays in £85. He works out that the balance should be £414. Is he correct?

   _____

Use rounding to say if the answers given might be correct or are definitely wrong.

5. a 345 × 22 = 7 590   b 17 × 3 402 = 25 883

   _____   _____

   _____   _____

   c 1 689 + 1 022 + 3 449 = 6 160

   _____

   _____

> **Remember**
>
> You can round bigger numbers to the nearest 100.

6. 3 241 people each paid £11 to attend an arts event held over three days. The manager calculates ticket sales to be £356 510. Is his calculation likely to be correct?

   _____

11 Negative numbers

First read this ...

Most of the numbers you deal with every day are positive, for example, the counting numbers 1, 2, 3, 4, 5...

In some practical situations, such as temperature, numbers can be negative.

Temperatures below zero are freezing, and are shown as negative numbers.

▷ A negative or minus sign written in front of a number, for example, –5, shows that it is negative.

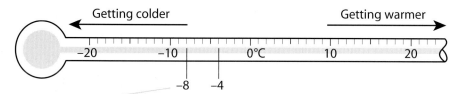

–8°C is colder than –4°C, so –8 is less than –4.

> **Tip**
>
> A common mistake is to think that –8 is bigger than –4, because 8 is greater than 4. Picture the numbers on a number line, to see which is bigger.

Now try it!

1. Here is a map of Great Britain showing the temperatures in some cities.

   a In which cities are temperatures above zero?

   _____

   b In which cities are temperatures below zero?

   _____

   c Which city has the highest temperature?

   _____

   d Which city has the lowest temperature?

   _____

   e Is the temperature below zero in Manchester?

   _____

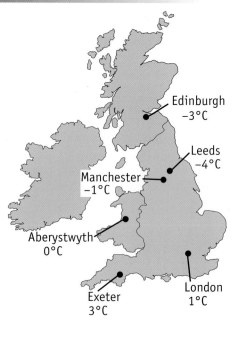

2. A woman has an overdraft facility of £200 with her cheque account. She has a balance of £85 and writes a cheque for £160. What is her new balance?

> **Tip**
>
> Draw part of a number line to help you work out the answer.

12 Remember what you have learned

First complete this ...

▷ Every digit in a number has a value, depending on its position in the number. This is called its _____ _____.

▷ The key digit is immediately to the right of the place value you are rounding to.

   ▷ Round _____ when the key digit is 5, 6, 7, 8 or 9.

   ▷ Round _____ when the key digit is 1, 2, 3 or 4.

▷ When you multiply a number by 10, all the digits in the number move _____ place to the left.

▷ When you multiply a number by 100, all the digits in the number move _____ places to the left.

▷ When you multiply a number by 1 000, all the digits in the number move _____ places to the left.

▷ When you divide a number by 10, all the digits in the number move _____ place to the right.

▷ When you divide a whole number by 100, all the digits in the number move _____ places to the right.

▷ Add and _____ are opposite operations.

▷ Multiply and _____ are opposite operations.

▷ A negative or minus sign written in front of a number, for example, –5, shows that it is _____.

Test tip

▪ Addition questions usually use the words **total** or **altogether**.

▪ **More** usually means you need to **add**.

▪ **Take** often means **subtract**.

▪ **How many more** or **how much more** usually tells you to **subtract**.

▪ A question that includes **shares** or **sharing** usually means you need to **divide**.

Now try it!

1. A customer's car needs a service at 48 000 miles. His car has done 33 650 miles.

   How many more miles can he drive the car before its service is needed?

   A ☐ 14 350   C ☐ 15 350

   B ☐ 14 450   D ☐ 16 650

2. A cable television company has 67 045 customers.

   What is this number, in words?

   A ☐ six million, seven thousand and forty-five

   B ☐ sixty-seven thousand and forty-five

   C ☐ six thousand, seven hundred and forty-five

   D ☐ sixty-seven hundred and forty-five

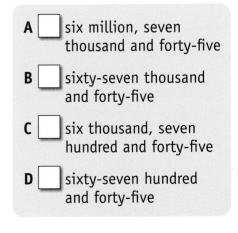

3. At a football match, 44 645 fans attended.

   What is this figure to the nearest hundred?

   A ☐ 44 650
   B ☐ 44 600
   C ☐ 44 640
   D ☐ 44 700

4. A printing business charges a fixed rate of £25 for a pair of printed T-shirts.

   What is the correct way to work out the cost of having 20 pairs of T-shirts printed?

   A ☐ £25 × 2
   B ☐ £25 × 10
   C ☐ £25 × 20
   D ☐ (£25 + £25) × 20

5. Thirty-nine thousand and five households receive a free newspaper every week.

   What is this number in figures?

   A ☐ 39 005
   B ☐ 3 905
   C ☐ 390 005
   D ☐ 30 905

6. One weekend, 86 000 people visited Clacton. The following weekend 139 270 people visited Clacton.

   How many more people went on the second weekend than the first?

   A ☐ 216 270
   B ☐ 990 270
   C ☐ 53 270
   D ☐ 44 270

7. A man sells 14 pictures for £50 each.
   How much money did he collect?

   A ☐ £140
   B ☐ £70
   C ☐ £700
   D ☐ £64

8. A group of seven friends win a total lottery prize of £2 583. They each have an equal share of £369.

   Which calculation can they use to check if this is correct?

   A ☐ 2 583 × 369
   B ☐ 369 ÷ 7
   C ☐ 2 583 × 7
   D ☐ 369 × 7

9. A hotel charges £65 for one person for one night.

   How much in total will it charge two people for three nights?

   A ☐ £195

   B ☐ £130

   C ☐ £390

   D ☐ £325

10. The table shows the average temperatures in Paris between November and February.

Temperatures in Paris (°C)			
Nov	Dec	Jan	Feb
–4	–2	0	4

    What is the lowest temperature?

    A ☐ –4°C

    B ☐ –2°C

    C ☐ 0°C

    D ☐ 4°C

11. A householder pays £876 a year in house insurance. She pays in twelve equal monthly instalments.

    How much does she pay per month?

    A ☐ £70.50

    B ☐ £76

    C ☐ £86

    D ☐ £73

12. A business makes £38 457 profit in June.

    What is this amount, to the nearest thousand?

    A ☐ £38 000

    B ☐ £38 500

    C ☐ £39 000

    D ☐ £40 000

13. A music store sells 760 CDs in one week, then 907 and 952 in the following two weeks.

    How many CDs does it sell in the three weeks?

    A ☐ 2 509

    B ☐ 2 519

    C ☐ 2 609

    D ☐ 2 619

14. What is the correct way to use rounding to check the answer to 28 × 832?

    A ☐ 20 × 830

    B ☐ 30 × 830

    C ☐ 20 × 840

    D ☐ 30 × 840

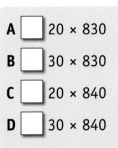

B Working with ratio and proportion

You should already know how to:

✓ multiply and divide two-digit numbers by single-digit numbers.

By the end of this section you will know how to:

▷▷ interpret simple ratio as the number of parts

▷▷ find quantities in a given ratio

▷▷ use direct proportion to increase or decrease quantities.

1 Understanding ratio

First read this ...

In a recipe, you use 1 part of fat for every 2 parts of flour. You can write this as a **ratio**:

fat : flour = 1 : 2

▷ A **ratio** is used to compare two or more quantities.

You write the quantities together with a colon (:) between them.

Example 1: What is the ratio of blue squares to yellow squares in this tiling pattern?

There are **7 yellow squares** and **8 blue squares**.

The question asks for the ratio of **blue to yellow**.

Answer: 8 : 7

Do not include units in ratios because they are comparing amounts of the same thing.

Example 2: A biscuit recipe takes 4 ounces of flour, 3 ounces of sugar and 1 ounce of butter. What is the ratio of butter to sugar to flour?

4 ounces flour, 3 ounces sugar, 1 ounce butter

Answer: 1 : 3 : 4

Tip

Another way to say the ratio **8 : 7** is 'eight to seven'.

Test tip

Make sure you write the ratio in the order that is asked for in the question.

You can **simplify** ratios by dividing each part by the same number.

> **Example 3:** Simplify these ratios.
> **a** 8:6 **b** £6 to £2 **c** £2 to 50p

a Divide 8 and 6 by 2. _____Answer: 4:3_____

b Omit the units. Divide both sides by 2. _____Answer: 3:1_____

c £2 is 200 pence. Omit the units. Divide both sides by 50.
_____Answer: 4:1_____

> **Tip**
> Always make sure that all parts are in the **same units** before you simplify a ratio.

▶▶ *Now try it!*

1. There are nine females and eleven males waiting in a health clinic.

   a What is the ratio of females to males? _____

   b What is the ratio of males to females? _____

2. Two friends have £5 and £7, respectively. What is the ratio of the first friend's money to the second friend's?

   _____

> **Tip**
> **Respectively** means 'in the order given'.

3. A biscuit recipe takes 5 ounces of flour, 3 ounces of sugar and 1 ounce of butter. What is the ratio of butter to sugar to flour?

   _____

4. Simplify these following ratios.

   a 8:4 _____   b 3:6 _____

   c 4:24 _____   d 10:15 _____

   e 25:15 _____   f 125:625 _____

   g £2:£4 _____   h £3:75p _____

   i 2:4:8 _____   j 4:10:12 _____

> **Tip**
> Make sure you divide all the parts by the same number.

5. There are five women and fifteen men working on a construction site. Write the ratio of women to men as a ratio in its simplest form.

   _____

6. Two friends are setting up a business, and have £25 and £250, respectively, to invest. What is the ratio of the first friend's money to the second friend's money?

   _____

> **Remember**
> Numbers that end in 0 or 5 can be divided by 5.

2 Using ratios to find quantities

First read this ...

For the ratio 2:1, there are three **parts** and two **shares**.

$$2 : 1$$
$$2 + 1 = 3$$

You can find out how much **one part** is worth by dividing the total.

> **Example 1:** A profit of £36 is to be divided between two business partners in the ratio 3:1.
> **a** How much does the first partner get?
> **b** How much does the second partner get?

Add the number of parts to find the total: 3 + 1 = 4
Divide the total amount by the total number of parts to find the value of 1 part: £36 ÷ 4 = £9

a The first partner gets three parts: 3 × £9   Answer: £27

b The second partner gets one part: 1 × £9   Answer: £9

> **Tip**
>
> Start by finding how many parts there are altogether. Divide the total quantity by this number to find what one part is worth.

> **Example 2:** A father and son won some money and decided to share it in the ratio of 4:5, respectively. The father's part of the winnings was £120. How much did the son win?

The father's share was four parts: 4 parts = £120
1 part: £120 ÷ 4 = £30
The son had five parts: 5 × £30   Answer: £150

> **Test tip**
>
> Always look carefully at the question. You may need to include units in your answers.

Now try it!

1. £24 is to be split between two friends in the ratio 1:5. How much does each friend get?

_____

2. Water in a swimming pool is treated with two chemicals mixed in the ratio of 5:4. The total volume of the chemicals is 45 litres. How much of each chemical is used?

_____

3. Concrete consists of six parts gravel to one part cement. A builder makes up 140 kg of concrete mixture. What is the weight of gravel used in this mixture?

_____

> **Tip**
>
> **Six parts to one part** means the ratio is 6 : 1.

4. A sum of money is shared between two boys in the ratio 3:4. If the first gets £21, how much does the second get?

_____

3 Direct proportion

First read this ...

In a recipe, to make **double** the amount, you multiply all the quantities by 2.

> **Example 1:** A recipe for four people takes 12 ounces of flour. How many ounces of flour would be needed if the same recipe is followed to feed:
> **a** 8 people   **b** 2 people   **c** 6 people?

a 8 is double 4, so double the amount of flour: $12 \times 2 = 24$

                      Answer: 24 ounces

b 2 is half of 4, so halve the amount of flour: $12 \div 2 = 6$

                      Answer: 6 ounces

c Divide 12 ounces by the number of people to find what 1 person needs: $12 \div 4 = 3$ ounces

Multiply this by the new number of people:

3 ounces $\times 6 = 18$ ounces   Answer: 18 ounces

The quantities in the recipe stay in the same **proportion**.

> ▷ Two quantities are in **direct proportion** if one quantity increases or decreases in the same way as the other increases or decreases.

Tip

To make half the amount, divide all the quantities by 2.

Tip

Use direct proportion when you are given **amounts** rather than **parts** (as in ratio).

Now try it!

1. This recipe is for three people.

   a How many eggs will you need for six people?

     _____

   b How much milk will you need for four people?

     _____

   c How much flour will you need for eight people?

     _____

Recipe: Pancakes
3 eggs
150 ml milk
450 g flour

2. Mixing 3 dessertspoons of custard powder with 450 ml of milk will make enough custard for two people.

   a What quantities of custard powder and milk do you need to make custard for four people?

     _____

   b How much milk should you mix with 1 dessertspoon of custard powder?

     _____

4 Remember what you have learned

First complete this ...

▷ A _____ is used to compare two or more quantities.

▷ To write a _____ comparing two or more quantities, write the amounts together with a colon (:) between them, for example, 3:1 or 1:3:6.

▷ Two quantities are in _____ _____ if one quantity increases or decreases in the same way as the other increases or decreases.

Now try it!

1. A cordial drink is a mixture of three parts lemonade to one part cordial.

   How much lemonade must be added to 3 pints of cordial?

   A ☐ 1 pint
   B ☐ 3 pints
   C ☐ 9 pints
   D ☐ 6 pints

2. A bricklayer mixes mortar using four parts sand to one part cement. He makes a mix that has 12 parts sand.

   How many parts of cement are there in the mix?

   A ☐ 3
   B ☐ 4
   C ☐ 8
   D ☐ 5

3. This recipe is for two cheese pastries.

   > Recipe: Cheese pastries
   > 100 g flour
   > 25 g grated cheese
   > 25 ml milk
   > 25 g butter

   A ☐ 100 g
   B ☐ 160 g
   C ☐ 200 g
   D ☐ 250 g

   What amount of grated cheese will be needed to make 16 cheese pastries?

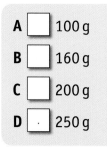

4. A hairdresser mixes a total of 36 ml of colour.
He uses twice as much copper colour as base colour.

Which colour mix is correct?

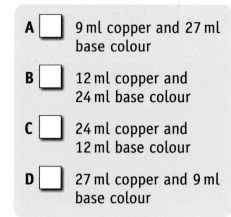

A ☐ 9 ml copper and 27 ml base colour

B ☐ 12 ml copper and 24 ml base colour

C ☐ 24 ml copper and 12 ml base colour

D ☐ 27 ml copper and 9 ml base colour

5. This recipe is for four fruit scones.

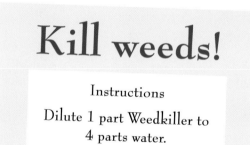

Recipe: Fruit scones
200 g flour
2 eggs
100 ml milk
500 g currants

A ☐ 30 g

B ☐ 300 g

C ☐ 400 g

D ☐ 1 200 g

How much flour will be needed to make six of these fruit scones?

6. The instructions on a bottle of weedkiller are given below.

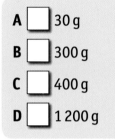

Kill weeds!

Instructions

Dilute 1 part Weedkiller to 4 parts water.

A ☐ 250 ml

B ☐ 1 000 ml

C ☐ 1 250 ml

D ☐ 2 500 ml

A gardener has 250 ml of weedkiller.

How much water should he add to this?

C Working with fractions

You should already know how to:

✓ read, write and understand common fractions

✓ recognise equivalent fractions.

By the end of this section you will know how to:

▷▷ read, write and compare common fractions

▷▷ use equivalent fractions to show quantities as fractions

▷▷ find fractions of whole-number quantities and measurements.

1 Understanding fractions

First read this ...

▷ A fraction is a part of a whole.

Three out of four squares are red.

Three out of four is the same as three quarters or $\frac{3}{4}$.

red squares   → 3 ← numerator (number on top)
total squares → 4 ← denominator (number on bottom)

This fraction wall shows how a **whole** can be split into **different fractions**.

1 equal part   → 1
2 equal parts   → $\frac{1}{2}$ s
3 equal parts   → $\frac{1}{3}$ s
4 equal parts   → $\frac{1}{4}$ s
5 equal parts   → $\frac{1}{5}$ s
6 equal parts   → $\frac{1}{6}$ s
7 equal parts   → $\frac{1}{7}$ s
8 equal parts   → $\frac{1}{8}$ s
9 equal parts   → $\frac{1}{9}$ s
10 equal parts → $\frac{1}{10}$ s

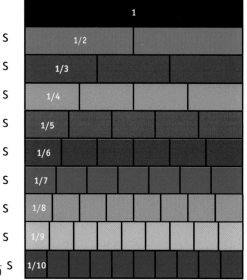

> **Tip**
>
> $\frac{1}{4}$ is smaller than $\frac{1}{3}$ because as you divide the whole into more parts, the fraction becomes smaller.

The fraction wall also shows which fractions show the same amount.

These are **equivalent fractions**, for example:

$$\frac{1}{2} = \frac{2}{4} = \frac{3}{6} = \frac{4}{8} = \frac{5}{10}$$

$$\frac{1}{4} = \frac{2}{8}$$

$$\frac{1}{3} = \frac{2}{6} = \frac{3}{9}$$

You find **equivalent** fractions by multiplying or by dividing the numerator and denominator of a fraction by the **same number**.

Example: Simplify $\frac{12}{16}$.

Choose a number to divide into the numerator and denominator (top and bottom).

12 and 16 can both be divided by 2.

$$\frac{12}{16} \xrightarrow{\div 2} \frac{6}{8} \qquad \frac{6}{8} \xrightarrow{\div 2} \frac{3}{4}$$

Answer: $\frac{3}{4}$

> **Tip**
>
> Dividing bottom and top of a fraction by the same number is called cancelling, or simplifying.

> **Tip**
>
> You can divide top and bottom by 4:
>
> $$\frac{12}{16} \xrightarrow{\div 4} \frac{3}{4}$$

▶▶ Now try it!

1. Write the following fractions in their lowest terms.

a $\frac{6}{12}$ _____

b $\frac{15}{75}$ _____

c $\frac{21}{35}$ _____

d $\frac{35}{56}$ _____

e $\frac{45}{72}$ _____

f $\frac{40}{100}$ _____

g $\frac{16}{64}$ _____

h $\frac{24}{60}$ _____

i $\frac{18}{27}$ _____

j $\frac{36}{12}$ _____

k $\frac{64}{80}$ _____

l $\frac{10}{1000}$ _____

> **Test tip**
>
> In answers, fractions should be simplified or written in their **lowest terms**.

> **Remember**
>
> Even numbers can be divided by 2 and numbers that end in 0 or 5 can be divided by 5. If neither applies, try dividing by 3 or 7.

First read this ...

To write one quantity as a fraction of another, put the first quantity on the top of the fraction, and the second quantity on the bottom.

Example 1: What is 5 out of 20 as a fraction?

In 5 out of 20:
5 is the first number,
20 is the second number.

$$\frac{5}{20} \overset{\div 5}{\underset{\div 5}{=}} \frac{1}{4}$$

Answer: $\frac{1}{4}$

Test tip

Always read the question carefully, to find out what you need to do.

To find a fraction of an amount or quantity, you divide:

▷ To find $\frac{1}{2}$ of a quantity, you divide by 2.

▷ To find $\frac{1}{3}$ of a quantity, you divide by 3.

▷ To find $\frac{1}{4}$ of something, you divide by 4.

▷ To find $\frac{1}{5}$ of something, you divide by 5 ... and so on.

Example 2: Find: **a** $\frac{1}{2}$ of £16 **b** $\frac{1}{3}$ of 18 cm.

a $\frac{1}{2}$ of £16 = £16 ÷ 2 = £8

Answer: £8

b $\frac{1}{3}$ of 18 cm = 18 cm ÷ 3 = 6 cm

Answer: 6 cm

To find $\frac{2}{3}$ of a quantity:

▷ find $\frac{1}{3}$: divide by 3

▷ find $\frac{2}{3}$: multiply by 2.

Remember

$\frac{2}{3}$ is 2 lots of $\frac{1}{3}$

$= 2 \times \frac{1}{3}$

Example 3: Find: **a** $\frac{2}{3}$ of £36 **b** $\frac{3}{4}$ of £12.

a $\frac{1}{3}$ of £36 = £36 ÷ 3 = £12

$\frac{2}{3}$ of £36 = £12 × 2 = £24

Answer: £24

b $\frac{1}{4}$ of £12 = £12 ÷ 4 = £3

$\frac{3}{4}$ of £12 = £3 × 3 = £9

Answer: £9

Tip

$\frac{3}{4}$ is 3 lots of $\frac{1}{4}$

$= 3 \times \frac{1}{4}$

▶ Now try it!

1. Write the following as fractions.

   a 6 out of 20 = _____   b 14 out of 21 = _____

   c 24 out of 36 = _____   d 25 out of 35 = _____

Remember

Simplify the fraction wherever possible.

2. In a safety test, a car scored 35 points out of a possible 40. Write this as a fraction in its simplest form.

   _____

3. Find the following fractions.

   a $\frac{1}{2}$ of 36 kg   _____   b $\frac{1}{4}$ of £32   _____

   c $\frac{1}{3}$ of 27 cm   _____   d $\frac{1}{5}$ of £30   _____

   e $\frac{1}{6}$ of 24 m   _____   f $\frac{1}{10}$ of £80   _____

   g $\frac{1}{8}$ of 16 g   _____   h $\frac{1}{4}$ of 28p   _____

4. A trainee IT worker spends one tenth of her earnings on leisure activities. If she earns £1 500 a month, how much does she spend on leisure activities each month?

   _____

Test tip

Test questions often ask for a fraction of a quantity, or for one quantity as a fraction of another.
Learn to deal with both types of question.

5. $\frac{1}{7}$ of a concrete mix is made of cement. How much cement is needed to make 56 kg of concrete?

   _____

6. Find:

   a $\frac{3}{4}$ of 16   _____   b $\frac{2}{3}$ of 48   _____

   c $\frac{2}{5}$ of 45   _____   d $\frac{3}{10}$ of 60   _____

   e $\frac{3}{8}$ of £48   _____   f $\frac{4}{5}$ of 45 cm   _____

7. One Saturday, 300 people go to the local cinema and $\frac{2}{5}$ of them pay the discount rate.
   How many people pay the discount rate?

8. Of 180 employees at a factory, three-quarters are female.

   a How many employees are female?

   _____

   b How many employees are male?

   _____

Test tip

Check your answers. The two parts should total 180.

First read this ...

▷ A fraction is a part of a _____ .

▷ To write one quantity as a fraction of another, put the first quantity on the _____ of the fraction, and the second quantity on the _____ .

▷ To find $\frac{1}{2}$ of a quantity you divide by _____ .

▷ To find $\frac{1}{3}$ of a quantity you divide by _____ .

▷ To find $\frac{1}{4}$ of something, you divide by _____ .

▷ To find $\frac{1}{5}$ of something, you divide by _____ .

▷ To find $\frac{2}{3}$ of a quantity:

  ▷ find $\frac{1}{3}$: divide by _____ .

  ▷ find $\frac{2}{3}$: multiply by _____ .

Now try it!

1. The diagram below shows four large glasses.

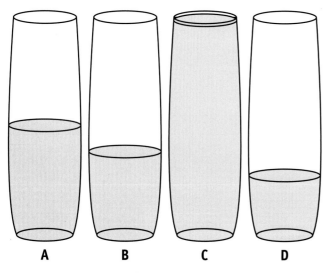

A
B
C
D

A B C D

Which one is approximately one third full?

2. An employer receives 36 job applications and decides to interview two-thirds of the applicants.

   How many applicants does she interview?

   A 54
   B 9
   C 12
   D 24

3. 1000 raffle tickets are sold at a dance for charity. There are ten prizes to be won.

   What fraction of tickets will win a prize?

   A ☐ $\frac{1}{1000}$

   B ☐ $\frac{1}{990}$

   C ☐ $\frac{1}{100}$

   D ☐ $\frac{1}{10}$

4. An optician examines 48 patients. Three-quarters of them need spectacles.

   How many of the patients need spectacles?

   A ☐ 12

   B ☐ 30

   C ☐ 36

   D ☐ 40

5. The table shows the ages of members at a local social club.

14–19	20–24
50	100

   What fraction of members are aged 20–24?

   A ☐ $\frac{1}{3}$

   B ☐ $\frac{2}{5}$

   C ☐ $\frac{2}{3}$

   D ☐ $\frac{4}{5}$

   Hint

   Find the total number of members first.

6. A train ticket costs £12.00. With a railcard, there is a discount of $\frac{1}{3}$ off ticket prices.

   How much is the discount?

   A ☐ £36

   B ☐ £3

   C ☐ £8

   D ☐ £4

7. Ten out of fifty runners complete a cross-country race in under an hour.

   What fraction is this?

   A ☐ $\frac{1}{5}$

   B ☐ $\frac{1}{4}$

   C ☐ $\frac{1}{3}$

   D ☐ $\frac{1}{10}$

D Working with decimals and money

You should already know how to:

✔ read, write and understand decimals

✔ add and subtract sums of money

✔ round amounts of money

✔ use a calculator to check answers.

By the end of this section, you will know how to:

▷▷ order and compare decimals with up to three decimal places

▷▷ add, subtract, multiply and divide with decimals and money

▷▷ multiply and divide decimals by 10 and 100

▷▷ estimate answers by rounding decimals.

---

1 Understanding decimals

First read this ...

▷ Decimal numbers have two parts: a **whole number** part and a **decimal part**.

▷ The two parts are separated by a decimal point.

3.2 metres means 3 whole metres and 2 tenths of a metre.

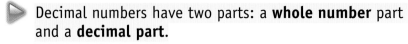
whole number part   decimal part

The number of digits after the decimal point is the number of decimal places.

whole number		decimal part		
units		tenths	hundredths	
3	.	2		one decimal place
1	.	2	5	two decimal places

You compare the size of decimal numbers by looking at the digits in each place-value position. Start with the largest place value.

> **Tip**
>
> You use and write numbers as decimals every day. Common examples include measures, such as length and weight, and money.

> **Tip**
>
> 3.456 means 3 units, 4 tenths, 5 hundredths and 6 thousandths.

Example 1: Put these lengths in order of size, starting with the largest: 2.7 m, 2.57 m, 3.7 m, 2.75 m.

Start by comparing the whole number parts first:
3 is bigger than 2 so 3.7 m is the largest.

Next compare tenths:
7 is bigger than 5, so the next largest length is 2.7 or 2.75.

Next compare hundredths:
2.7 means 2.70. 5 is bigger than 0 so 2.75 is bigger than 2.7.

This leaves 2.7, then 2.57.

Answer: 3.7 m, 2.75 m, 2.7 m, 2.57 m

▷ There are 100 pence in every pound.

Example 2: Write £2.05 in pence.

£2.05 is 2 × 100p + 5p = 205p

Answer: 205p

Tip

Use a place-value table. Put in zeros to line up the numbers.

U		t	h
2	.	7	0
2	.	5	7
3	.	7	0
2	.	7	5

Tip

Never use 'p' with the £ sign.

▶▶ *Now try it!*

1. Put these lengths in order of size, starting with the largest.

   a 3.22 m, 3.2 m, 2.3 m, 3.23 m

   b 10.7 cm, 10.07 cm, 10.777 cm, 10.707 cm, 10.007 cm

   c 5.30 km, 3.55 km, 3.505 km, 5.55 km, 5.305 km

2. Write these sums of money in order, starting with the smallest.

   a £0.02, £2.22, £2.20, £0.22

   b £3.33, £3.03, £33.30, £0.33, £30.03

   c £15.17, £17.05, £17.15, £15.10, £15.07

3. Write these amounts in pence.

   a £3.50   b £0.65   c £0.03

4. Write these amounts in pounds.

   a 555p   b 20p   c 5p

2 Calculating with decimals

First read this ...

You calculate with decimals using the same methods as for whole numbers.

> **Example 1:** An athlete runs 5.4 km on Friday, 4.69 km on Saturday and 11.85 km on Sunday. How far does she run, in total, from Friday to Sunday?

> **Tip**
>
> **In total** usually means 'add'.

Write the numbers with the decimal points lined up.

Add the columns, from right to left, in the usual way.

	5	.	4	0	
	4	.	6	9	+
1_1	1_1	.	8_1	5	
2	1	.	9	4	

— Write 0 here, to help add the digits in columns.

Answer: 21.94 km

> **Test tip**
>
> Check your answer makes sense. Add the whole number parts: 5 + 4 + 11 = 20.

> **Example 2:** An empty suitcase weighs 1.92 kg. When packed, it weighs 6.2 kg. How much do the contents of the suitcase weigh?

Subtract the weight of the empty suitcase from the weight of the packed suitcase.

Write the numbers with the decimal points lined up.

Subtract in columns, from right to left, in the usual way.

^{5}6	.	^{11}2	^{1}0	
1	.	9	2	–
4	.	2	8	

— Write 0 here, to show you are subtracting from the final zero.

Answer: 4.28 kg

> **Tip**
>
> Use the method of subtraction you prefer, for example, 'borrowing' or 'paying back'.

▷ To multiply a decimal number by 10 or 100, move all the digits one or two places to the left.

▷ To divide a decimal number by 10 or 100, move all the digits one or two places to the right.

> **Tip**
>
> Multiplying a number by 10 or 100 makes it 10 or 100 times bigger. This is why all the digits move to the left: the place value of each digit increases.

Example 3: Calculate: a 2.45×10 b $65.2 \div 100$.

a $2.45 \times 10 =$

T	U		t	h
	2	.	4	5
2	4	.	5	0

Answer: 24.5

b $65.2 \div 100 =$

T	U		t	h	th
6	5	.	2		
	6	.	5	2	
	0	.	6	5	2

Answer: 0.652

▶▶ *Now try it!*

1. Work out:

   a 4.23 + 5.66 _____ b £4.69 + £5.98 _____

   c 8.45 – 4.07 _____ d 4.5 – 3.22 _____

2. Ring the correct answer.

   a 6.7 + 0.88 　　A 6.95 　　B 7.58

   b £6.67 – £5.09 　　A £1.58 　　B £0.77

3. One piece of rope is 66.4 m long and another is 98.7 m. What is the combined length of the two pieces of rope?

   _____

4. A boy runs 100 metres in 12.38 seconds. His older brother runs the same distance in 10.8 seconds. What is the difference between their times?

   _____

5. The sign shows today's bargains at a local supermarket. A customer buys one roast chicken and two meat pies.

   a How much does the customer pay?

   _____

   b The same customer pays with a ten-pound note. How much change should he receive?

   _____

Today's special offer	
Cornish pasties	69p
Meat pies	75p
Roast chickens	£3.75

6. Ring the correct answer.

   a 1.32 × 10 　　A 13.2 　　B 132

   b £0.06 × 100 　　A £0.60 　　B £6.00

   c 100 × 5.4 pence 　　A £5.40 　　B £54.00

   Test tip

   Make sure the amounts are either all in pounds or all in pence first.

7. A farm worker is paid £6.90 an hour. How much is she paid for working ten hours?

   _____

8. Electricity costs 12.42 pence per unit. How much does it cost, in pounds, for 100 units of electricity?

   _____

9. Ring the correct answer.

   a £50.20 ÷ 10 　　A £5.02 　　B £5.20

   b 1.6 ÷ 100 　　A 0.16 　　B 0.016

10. A carpenter cuts a plank of wood 5 metres long into 10 equal lengths. How long is each length?

    _____

Multiplying decimals

First read this ...

When you multiply decimals you have to think carefully about where to place the decimal point.

One decimal place in the question means one decimal place in the answer.

Example 1: Calculate 22.5 × 5.

Do the multiplication but ignore the decimal points.

Count the decimal places in the question:

$$
\begin{array}{r}
225 \\
5 \times \\
\hline
1\,125 \\
\end{array}
$$

There is one decimal place in 22.5, and none in 5.
This gives a total of one decimal place.

Look at the answer: 1125
Insert the decimal point to give one decimal place: 112.5

Answer: 112.5

Test tip

Check your answer to be sure it makes sense: 22 × 5 = 110

This method is useful for multiplying numbers by 1.5.

Test tip

You are often asked to multiply by 1.5 in tests.

Example 2: Calculate 2.5 × 1.5.

1.5 is the same as $1\frac{1}{2}$.

1 × 2.5 =   2.50 ← Write 0 here, to keep
$\frac{1}{2}$ of 2.5 = 2.50 ÷ 2 = 1.25 + the digits in columns.
Add: ―――
                  3.75

Answer: 3.75

Remember

To find half of a number, just divide by 2.

You can break a problem into separate calculations to make it easier.

Example 3: Calculate 12.50 × 30.

As 30 = 3 × 10, so 12.50 × 30
              = 12.50 × 3 × 10.

First, multiply 12.50 by 3:   12.50 × 3 = 37.50

Then, multiply the result by 10:   37.50 × 10 = 375.0

Answer: 375

Tip

$$
\begin{array}{r}
1250 \\
3 \times \\
\hline
3750 \\
\end{array}
$$

12.50 has 2 decimal places so insert the decimal point: 37.50

▶▶ *Now try it!*

1. Use any method to work these out, but do not use a calculator.

   a 4.5×5 b 6.4×3 c 2.5×6

   _____   _____   _____

   d 12.5×5 e 5.4×40 f 2.15×30

   _____   _____   _____

2. Work these out.

   a 22×1.5 b 12.6×1.5

   _____   _____

3. A magazine article recommends everyone to drink 2.5 litres of water a day. How many litres of water is this in a week?

   _____

4. One hundred and fifty people each pay £1.50 for a ticket. How much did they pay in total?

   _____

   > **Tip**
   >
   > You need to calculate 150 lots of £1.50. Treat £1.50 as 1.5, but remember to put units in the answer.

5. A builder's assistant is paid £6.30 an hour. He works for six hours. How much does he get paid?

   _____

6. An office worker earns £5.70 per hour and works for 40 hours. How much does he earn?

   _____

7. Drinks at a party cost £1.50 each. 250 people buy one drink each. How much do they pay altogether?

   _____

4 Dividing with decimals

First read this ...

You need to be able to divide a decimal by a whole number. Align the decimal points first.

Example 1: Calculate 822.4 ÷ 4.

Put the decimal point in first:

$$4)\overline{8\ 2\ 2\ .\ \overset{.}{4}}$$

Now divide:

$$4)\overline{8\ 2^2 2\ .^2 4}\ \ \underline{2\ 0\ 5\ .\ 6}$$

4 divides into 8 exactly, 8 ÷ 4 is 2.

4 does not divide into 2, so write 0, carry 2.

4 divides into 22 giving 5 with 2 left over.

4 divides into 24 exactly, giving 6.

Answer: 205.6

Example 2: A woman pays £870.00 a year for car insurance. She pays in 12 equal monthly instalments. How much does she pay each month?

You need to share £870 into 12 equal amounts.

Put the decimal point in first:

$$12)\overline{8\ 7\ 0\ .\ \overset{.}{0}\ 0}$$

Now divide:

$$12)\overline{8\ 7^3 0\ .^6 0\ 0}\ \ \underline{7\ 2\ .\ 5\ 0}$$

12 divides into 87 giving 7 with 3 left over.

12 divides into 30 giving 2 with 6 left over.

12 divides into 60 giving exactly 5.

Answer: £72.50

▷ To find a fraction of an amount:

   ▷ multiply by the numerator

   ▷ divide by the denominator.

Example 3: Find $\frac{2}{3}$ of £9.18.

First find $\frac{1}{3}$: £9.18 ÷ 3 = £3.06

$\frac{2}{3}$ is double $\frac{1}{3}$ so double this: £3.06 × 2 = £6.12

Answer: £6.12

Remember

Look back to page 16 to remind yourself how to divide.

Tip

Use times tables to help you with long division.
1 × 12 = 12
2 × 12 = 24
...
7 × 12 = 84

Remember

Amounts in pounds are written with two places of decimals, so write £72.50, not £72.5.

▶▶ *Now try it!*

1. Work these out without using a calculator.

   a $4\overline{)32.4}$ b $5\overline{)12.5}$

   c $302.4 \div 2$ _____   d $102.5 \div 5$ _____

   e $6\overline{)31.2}$ f $5\overline{)303.5}$

2. A group of five people were paid £72.50 for a job. They shared the money equally. How much did each person receive?

   _____

3. Six friends shared the cost of a meal. The bill came to £78.12. How much did they each pay?

   _____

4. A householder paid £436.80 for gas in a year. She paid in 12 equal monthly instalments. How much did she pay each month?

   _____

5. The fabric on a roll is 18 metres long. It is cut into 40 pieces of equal length. How long is each piece, in metres?

   _____

   > **Tip**
   >
   > To divide by 40 divide by 10 first, and then divide the result by 4.

6. Calculate:

   a $\frac{1}{3}$ of £6.24   _____   b $\frac{2}{3}$ of £4.32 _____

   c $\frac{1}{4}$ of 8.4 metres _____   d $\frac{3}{4}$ of £12.08 _____

7. The price of a train ticket that normally costs £8.31 is reduced by $\frac{1}{3}$ in a 'summer special' offer. How much is the discount?

   _____

8. A woman earns £344.80 per week. She spends $\frac{3}{4}$ of it on rent and food. How much does she spend on rent and food?

   _____

5 Decimal problems

Some problems take more than one step to solve them.

Example 1: A shop sells cans of drink for 52p each. A boy buys seven cans and pays for them with a £5 note. What change should he get?

First, choose the operations that are needed: *multiplication* (7 lots of 52p) and *subtraction* (taking the cost away from £5).

The cost of seven cans, in pence: 52p × 7 = 364p

Convert pence to pounds: 364p = £3.64

Subtract this from £5 to find the change: £5.00 – £3.64 = £1.36

Answer: £1.36

> **Tip**
>
> Adding, subtracting, multiplying and dividing are all called **operations**.

Sometimes you just need to be able to decide which method to use.

Example 2: An electricity company charges £12.50 each month for supplying the electricity and £0.12 for every unit of electricity used. A customer uses 250 units of electricity in one month. What is the correct way of calculating the bill for that month?

Multiply £0.12 by the number of units first and then *add* the £12.50 charge.

Answer: 250 × £0.12 + £12.50 **or** £0.12 × 250 + £12.50

> **Tip**
>
> These two answers are the same because you can **multiply** in any order.

You can use **reverse calculations** to check the results of calculations.

Example 3: A woman buys a loaf of bread for £1.80 and two tins of fish at £1.45 each. The total bill is £4.70. Which reverse calculation can she use to check the bill?

First, work out how the answer was found: by *adding* £1.80, £1.45 and £1.45.

To check this, do the reverse. Start with the total and *subtract* the cost of each item: £4.70 – £1.45 – £1.45 – £1.80 = £0.00.

Since the answer is £0.00, the original total is correct, because the woman started adding from £0.00.

Answer: £4.70 – £1.45 – £1.45 – £1.80

> **Remember**
>
> Reverse calculations are also called **inverse operations**:
> + and – are inverse operations
> × and ÷ are inverse operations

> **Test tip**
>
> The test will usually include a question asking you to check an answer using reverse calculations.

Now try it!

1. A shop sells small packets of biscuits for 47p each. A man buys six packets. How much change should he get from a £5 note?

_____

_____

2. The menu for a café is shown. A boy buys two cans of drink and an ice-cream. How much does it cost him?

_____

_____

Menu Refreshments:	
Cans of cold drink	47p
Ice-cream	£1.20
Popcorn	99p

3. A phone company charges a standard rate of £12 each month and 3p per minute for calls. A woman makes 150 minutes of calls in one month. How much is she charged for the month?

_____

_____

4. The normal price of fuel is 93.6p per litre. A customer has a voucher for '2p off' each litre of fuel. She buys 10 litres of fuel. How much does she pay?

_____

_____

5. A woman has £450 in her bank account. She pays £182 into the account and then writes cheques from her bank account for £256 and £83.67. What calculation does she need to do in order to work out her new bank balance?

_____

_____

Tip

In questions 5 and 6 you need to work out the calculation, _not_ find the answer.

6. A part-time assistant in a music shop earns £6.80 per hour. One week he is paid £306. What calculation would show how many hours he worked that week?

_____

_____

7. A girl buys two chocolate bars for 45p each and a can of drink for 52p. She is charged £1.42. What calculation can she do to check this charge?

_____

_____

6 Rounding decimal amounts

First read this ...

You can round decimal numbers to the **nearest whole number**, **tenth** or **hundredth**.

▷ To round to the nearest tenth, round to one decimal place.

▷ To round to the nearest hundredth, round to two decimal places.

Look for the **key digit**: if it is worth 5 or more, round up, and if it is worth less than 5, round down.

To round a decimal number to a whole number, the key digit is immediately after the decimal point.

Example 1: Round each number to the nearest whole number: **a** 3.4   **b** 8.54

a The key digit is 4; this is less than 5, so round down, leaving the whole-number part the same.   Answer: 3

b The key digit is 5, so round up, increasing the whole-number part by 1.   Answer: 9

To round a decimal number to one decimal place, the key digit is the second digit after the decimal point.

Example 2: Round each number to one decimal place:
a 4.65   **b** 56.982

a The key digit is 5, so round up from 6 to 7.   Answer: 4.7

b The key digit is 8, so round 9 up by 1, giving 57.0. Put the zero in to show there is one decimal place.   Answer: 57.0

> **Tip**
>
> When you round numbers to one decimal place, your answer should only have one digit after the decimal point.

You round the numbers in a calculation to **estimate** the answer.

Example 3: A receptionist is paid £6.20 per hour. She works for 39 hours a week. What calculation could you do to estimate her total pay for the week?

First, round the numbers: £6.20 to £6 and 39 to 40

Next, multiply: £6 × 40 = £240

Answer: £6 × 40

> **Test tip**
>
> Read the question carefully. You are asked for the calculation, not the answer.

▶▶ Now try it!

1. Round these decimal numbers to the nearest whole number.

   a 7.6   b 12.89   c 6.567

   _____   _____   _____

2. A vet weighs a dog and finds it weighs 26.7 kilograms. What is the dog's weight, to the nearest kilogram?

   _____

3. A householder reads her electricity meter: 2395.56

   What is the reading, to the nearest whole number?

   _____

4. A bank teller uses his calculator to work out 500 ÷ 37. The display on his calculator shows: 13.513513

   Round the answer to the nearest whole number.

   _____

5. Round these decimal numbers to the nearest tenth.

   a 5.63   b 12.856   c 6.899

   _____   _____   _____

Remember

Rounding to the nearest tenth means rounding to one decimal place.

6. A measuring jug contains 1.872 litres of lemonade. What is the volume of lemonade, to the nearest tenth of a litre?

   _____

7. Round these amounts to the nearest 10p.

   a £24.45   b 15.63   c £7.99

   _____   _____   _____

Tip

10p = £0.10

8. Round these decimal numbers to the nearest hundredth.

   a 6.375   b 0.403   c 23.498

   _____   _____   _____

Remember

Rounding to the nearest hundredth means rounding to two decimal places.
The key digit is the third digit after the decimal point.

9. A parcel waiting for delivery weighs 3.455 kg. Round this weight to two decimal places.

   _____

10. A man who earns £7.10 per hour works for 19 hours. What calculation can you do to estimate his pay?

    _____

11. Eleven people went out to dinner. Each meal cost £9.75. What calculation can they do to estimate the total bill?

    _____

7

Remember what you have learned

First complete this ...

▷ Decimal numbers have two parts: a _____ _____ part and a _____ part.

▷ The two parts are separated by a _____ point.

▷ There are 100 pence in every _____.

▷ To multiply a decimal number by 10 or 100, move all the digits one or two places to the _____.

▷ To divide a decimal number by 10 or 100, move all the digits one or two places to the _____.

▷ To find a fraction of an amount:

  ▷ multiply by the _____

  ▷ divide by the _____.

▷ To round to the nearest _____, round to one decimal place.

▷ To round to the nearest _____, round to two decimal places.

Now try it!

1. A man writes a cheque for two hundred and two pounds and two pence.

    How does he write this amount in figures?

    A ☐ £202.02

    B ☐ £202.2

    C ☐ £220.20

    D ☐ £220.02

2. A customer buys five packets of biscuits and two cakes in the supermarket.

    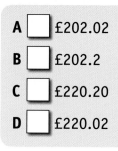

    How much does he pay in total?

    A ☐ £2.28

    B ☐ £5.44

    C ☐ £6.93

    D ☐ £3.77

3. The owner of a furniture store sells a desk for £156.99 and a table for £85.50. She calculates the total as £242.49.

    What calculation can she use to check her answer?

    A ☐ £156.99 – £85.50

    B ☐ £85.50 – £242.49

    C ☐ £242.49 + £85.50

    D ☐ £242.49 – £156.99

4. A boy buys seven chocolate bars for 47 pence each. He pays for them with a £5 note.

   What change should he get?

   A ☐ £1.29

   B ☐ £2.71

   C ☐ £3.29

   D ☐ £1.71

5. A householder reads her electricity meter.

   45675.54

   What is the reading, to the nearest whole number?

   A ☐ 45 680

   B ☐ 45 675

   C ☐ 45 676

   D ☐ 45 670

6. In a supermarket, a man picks up shopping that totals £35.17. As he has only £35 in vouchers, he decides to put back a jar of coffee costing £3.49.

   How much is the new total?

   A ☐ £30.68

   B ☐ £31.68

   C ☐ £31.58

   D ☐ £31.78

7. An assistant at a garden centre is paid £7.90 per hour. She works 39 hours per week.

   Which of these is the closest estimate of her total pay for the week?

   A ☐ £7 × 30

   B ☐ £8 × 30

   C ☐ £7 × 40

   D ☐ £8 × 40

8. At a charity event 1 875 cakes were sold for 20 pence each. The money collected came to £375.

   Which of these calculations could be used to check the amount is correct?

   A ☐ 375 ÷ 20

   B ☐ 375 − 0.2

   C ☐ 3 750 ÷ 20

   D ☐ 375 × 100 ÷ 20

9. When a charity organises a dance, four hundred and fifty people each pay £1.50 per ticket.

   How much do they pay altogether?

   A ☐ £67.50

   B ☐ £675.00

   C ☐ £6 750

   D ☐ £67 500

E Working with percentages

You should already know how to:

✓ recognise and use common equivalent fractions

✓ read, write and understand decimals.

By the end of this section you will know how to:

▷ recognise equivalences between common fractions, percentages and decimals

▷ calculate percentages of quantities or measures

▷ calculate percentage increases and decreases

▷ express one quantity as a percentage of another.

1 Understanding percentage

First read this ...

▷ A percentage is a number out of 100.

A percentage is the numerator of a fraction, when the denominator is 100: 20% means 20 out of 100.

The grid shows 100 equal squares.

50 squares (half of the grid) are coloured blue.

$\frac{50}{100}$ is 50%.

▷ $\frac{50}{100} = \frac{1}{2}$, so 50% = $\frac{1}{2}$.

25 squares (one quarter of the grid) are coloured red.

$\frac{25}{100}$ is 25%.

▷ $\frac{25}{100} = \frac{1}{4}$, so 25% = $\frac{1}{4}$.

10 squares (one tenth of the grid) are coloured green.

$\frac{10}{100}$ is 10%.

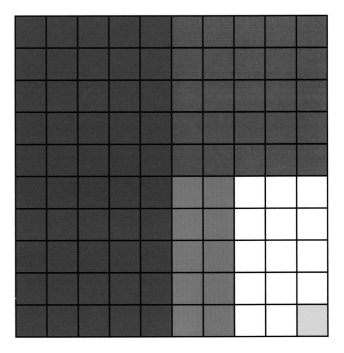

▷ $\frac{10}{100} = \frac{1}{10}$, so 10% = $\frac{1}{10}$.

1 square (one hundredth of the grid) is coloured yellow.

$\frac{1}{100}$ is 1%.

To change a percentage into a fraction or a decimal, write it over 100.

You can reduce it to its simplest form by dividing top and bottom by the same number.

Example 1: Write 20% as: **a** a decimal **b** a fraction.

a $20\% = \frac{20}{100}$

$= 20 \div 100$

$= 0.2$

Answer: 0.2

b $20\% = \frac{20}{100} = \frac{2}{10} = \frac{1}{5}$

$\div 10 \qquad \div 2$

$\div 10 \qquad \div 2$

Answer: $\frac{1}{5}$

Tip

You can also say:

20% is double 10%

10% = 0.1

2 × 0.1 = 0.2

Now try it!

1. Write 75% as:

   a a decimal —————————

   b a fraction —————————

Tip

75% is the same as 25% plus 50%.

2. Work out the missing decimals and fractions and write them in the table.

	Percentage	Fraction	Decimal
a	50%	$\frac{1}{2}$	
b	25%		
c	10%		0.1
d	30%		
e	40%		
f	5%		

3. Match each percentage to its equivalent fraction or decimal.

50%   30%   75%   60%   3%   80%

0.3   0.03 $\frac{4}{5}$ $\frac{1}{2}$ $\frac{3}{5}$ $\frac{3}{4}$

2 Percentages of quantities

First read this ...

▷ 50% is a half so, to find 50% of an amount, you halve it or divide by 2.

Example 1: What is 50% of 30?

$50\% = \frac{1}{2}$　　　$\frac{1}{2}$ of 30 = 15　　　　Answer: 15

Example 2: What is 50% of £24?

$\frac{1}{2}$ of £24 = £12　　　　　　Answer: £12

▷ To find 10% of an amount you divide by 10.

10% of £1.00 is £1.00 ÷ 10 = £0.10.

Example 3: What is 20% of £6.40?

To find 10% of an amount, divide by 10:
£6.40 ÷ 10 = £0.64
20% is double 10%:　2 × £0.64 = £1.28

Answer: £1.28

Example 4: Find 5% of 250 ml.

10% of 250 ml = 25 ml
5% is half of 10%, so 25 ml ÷ 2 = 12.5 ml

Answer: 12.5 ml

Example 5: 25 624 people went to a pop concert. 50% of them bought their ticket online. How many people bought their tickets online?

First, work out what the question is asking for:
50% of 25 624 = 25 624 ÷ 2 = 12 812

Answer: 12 812 people

Example 6: A car was worth £12 000 when it was new. It lost 75% of its value in the first year. By how much had it decreased in value in the first year?

First, work out what the question is asking for:
75% of £12 000

50% of £12 000 = £6 000　　　25% of £12 000 = £3 000

75% = 50% + 25% = £6 000 + £3 000

Answer: £9 000

Tip

Use 10% to find other amounts:

20% = 10% × 2.
Find 10% then multiply by 2.

5% = 10% ÷ 2.
Find 10% then divide by 2.

Remember

To find half of an amount, you divide by 2.

Test tip

Read a question all the way through and make sure you understand exactly what it asks.

Remember

75% = 50% + 25%

▶▶ *Now try it!*

1. Circle the methods you could use to calculate 25% of £6.40.

   A halve £6.40, then halve the answer

   B divide £6.40 by 25

   C divide £6.40 by four

   D multiply £6.40 by 25, then divide by 100

   E multiply £6.40 by 100, then divide by 25

   F divide £6.40 by ten to find 10%
   halve this answer to find 5%
   then add 10%, 10% and 5%

> **Remember**
>
> $50\% = \frac{1}{2}$
> $25\% = \frac{1}{4}$
> $75\% = \frac{3}{4}$

2. Find the following amounts.

   a 50% of 48

   b 50% of 74

   c 25% of 16

   d 75% of 120

3. To buy a car costing £2 400, a woman has to pay a deposit of 25%. How much is this?

4. A house that was worth £59 000 three years ago has now increased its value by 50%. How much is this increase?

5. Find the following amounts.

   a 10% of £40

   b 10% of £66

   c 20% of £8

   d 20% of £3.20

   e 5% of £60

   f 5% of £900

   g 30% of £4

   h 20% of £6.20

6. A man earns £285 a week. This is due to increase by 10%. How much is the increase?

7. The price of a DVD player is reduced in a sale by 20%. If it normally costs £90, what is the discount?

3 One quantity as a percentage of another

You need to be able to find one quantity as a percentage of another.

▷ To find one quantity as a percentage of another:

   ▷ divide the first quantity by the second: $\frac{first}{second}$

   ▷ then multiply the answer by 100%: $\frac{first}{second} \times 100\%$

It helps if you simplify the fraction $\frac{first}{second}$.

Test tip

If you see the phrase 'as a percentage' in a question, write the amount before it on top and the number following it underneath, then multiply by 100%.

Example 1: What is 5 as a percentage of 20?

First, divide 5 by 20: $\frac{5}{20}$ Simplify: $\frac{5}{20} \xrightarrow{\div 4} = \xrightarrow{\div 4} \frac{1}{4}$

Then multiply the answer by 100%: $\frac{1}{4} \times 100\% = 25\%$

Answer: 25%

Example 2: Out of 80 guests staying at a hotel, 60 had the full cooked breakfast. What percentage of guests had the full cooked breakfast?

First, divide 60 by 80: $\frac{60}{80}$ Simplify: $\frac{60}{80} \xrightarrow{\div 20} = \xrightarrow{\div 20} \frac{3}{4}$

$\frac{3}{4} \times 100\% = 75\%$

Answer: 75%

Example 3: A company made £4 million profit in 2004 and £2 million profit in 2005. What was the profit in 2005 as a percentage of the profit in 2004?

First, divide £2 000 000 by £4 000 000: $\frac{£2\,000\,000}{£4\,000\,000}$

Simplify: $\frac{£2\,000\,000}{£4\,000\,000} \xrightarrow{\div 2} = \xrightarrow{\div 2} \frac{1}{2}$

$\frac{1}{2} \times 100\% = 50\%$

Answer: 50%

Example 4: A group of friends spent £250 on organising a shared birthday party. They spent £100 of this on drinks. What percentage of the total did they spend on drinks?

First, divide £100 by £250: $\frac{£100}{£250}$ Simplify: $\frac{£100}{£250} \xrightarrow{\div 50} = \xrightarrow{\div 50} \frac{2}{5}$

$\frac{2}{5} \times 100\% = 40\%$

Answer: 40%

▶▶ *Now try it!*

1. What is 15 as a percentage of 60?

   _____

2. What is 16 as a percentage of 80?

   _____

Remember

To find $\frac{3}{4}$, divide by 4 then multiply by 3.

3. What is 8 as a percentage of 160?

   _____

4. What is 15 as a percentage of 50?

   _____

5. What is 36 as a percentage of 180?

   _____

6. What is 20 as a percentage of 400?

   _____

7. What is 12 kg as a percentage of 60 kg?

   _____

8. A garage MOT tested 40 cars in one week. 36 cars passed the test. What percentage passed?

   _____

9. A woman's weekly pay is £350. She receives a bonus of £70. Express the bonus as a percentage of her weekly pay.

   _____

10. The normal price of a two-week package holiday is advertised as £800. As a special offer, it is £200 cheaper. Express the saving as a percentage of the normal cost.

    _____

11. In a street there are 80 residents. 24 of them went to a meeting to discuss a proposed skate park. What percentage of the residents went to the meeting?

    _____

12. A company has 300 workers. 27 people work in the sales department. What percentage of the company work in the sales department?

    _____

13. A city has 15 leisure centres. Twelve of them will be closed on New Year's Day. What percentage of the leisure centres will be closed on New Year's Day?

    _____

First read this …

Interest added on to savings in a bank account may be expressed as a **percentage increase**.

You increase an amount by adding on.

▷ If an amount is **increased**, the new amount is **more than 100%**.

Example 1: Increase 80 by 10%.

First find 10% of 80: 10% of 80 = 8

The question is about percentage increase, so add: 80 + 8

Answer: 88

You can do the increase in one calculation:

100% + 10% = 110%

$$110\% \text{ of } 80 = \frac{\overset{11}{\cancel{110}}}{\underset{10}{\cancel{100}}} \times 80$$

$$= \frac{11}{\underset{1}{\cancel{10}}} \times \cancel{80}^{8}$$

$$= 11 \times 8$$

$$= 88$$

Price reduction in a sale may be expressed as a **percentage decrease**.

You decrease an amount by taking away.

▷ If an amount is **decreased**, the new amount is **less than 100%**.

Example 2: Decrease 80 by 25%.

First find 25% of 80: $\frac{1}{4}$ of 80 = 20

The question is about percentage decrease, so take away:
80 – 20

Answer: 60

You can do the decrease in one calculation:

100% – 25% = 75%

$$75\% \text{ of } 80 = \frac{3}{4} \times 80$$

$$= \frac{3}{\underset{1}{\cancel{4}}} \times \cancel{80}^{20}$$

$$= 3 \times 20$$

$$= 60$$

▶▶ *Now try it!*

1. Increase 60 by 10%.

   _____

   _____

2. Decrease 40 by 10%.

   _____

   _____

3. Increase 84 by 20%.

   _____

   _____

4. Decrease 76 by 20%.

   _____

   _____

5. Increase 46 by 5%.

   _____

   _____

6. Decrease 46 by 5%.

   _____

   _____

7. A man earns £285 a week. This is due to increase by 10%. How much will his new wage be?

   _____

   _____

> **Test tip**
>
> Ask yourself whether the question is asking for the new increased number, or just the increase.

8. A woman puts £2000 into a savings account. The interest rate is 5% per annum. How much will she have in her account after one year, including the interest?

   _____

   _____

> **Tip**
>
> 'Per annum' means each year.

First complete this ...

▷ A percentage is a number out of _____.

▷ $\frac{50}{100} = \frac{1}{2}$, so _____% = $\frac{1}{2}$.

▷ $\frac{25}{100} = \frac{1}{4}$, so _____% = $\frac{1}{4}$.

▷ $\frac{10}{100} = \frac{1}{10}$, so _____% = $\frac{1}{10}$.

▷ 50% is a half so, to find 50% of an amount, you _____ it or divide by _____.

▷ To find 10% of an amount you divide by _____.

▷ To find one quantity as a percentage of another:

  ▷ _____ the first quantity by the second: $\frac{first}{second}$

  ▷ then _____ the answer by 100%: $\frac{first}{second} \times 100\%$

▷ If an amount is increased, the new amount is _____ _____ than 100%.

▷ If an amount is decreased, the new amount is _____ _____ than 100%.

Test tip

The three types of percentage question commonly asked in the test are:
■ find the percentage of a quantity
■ increase or decrease a number by a given percentage
■ express one quantity as a percentage of another.
Learn how to do them all.

Now try it!

1. Of 900 people who went to a concert, 60% of them were female.

   How many were female?

   A ☐ 150
   B ☐ 360
   C ☐ 600
   D ☐ 540

2. Of the members at a gym, two-fifths were sent by their doctors, to lose weight.

   What is two-fifths as a percentage?

   A ☐ 12%
   B ☐ 20%
   C ☐ 25%
   D ☐ 40%

3. Of the residents in a street, 75% subscribe to satellite TV.

   What fraction of the residents subscribe to satellite TV?

   A ☐ $\frac{3}{4}$
   B ☐ $\frac{1}{4}$
   C ☐ $\frac{1}{3}$
   D ☐ $\frac{1}{2}$

4. A man has seen a mountain bike at his local shop, on sale for £402. The price for the same bike, in another shop, is 20% lower.

   How much can the man save if he buys the bike at the second shop?

   A ☐ £8.04

   B ☐ £20.10

   C ☐ £40.20

   D ☐ £80.40

5. What is one tenth as a percentage?

   A ☐ 100%

   B ☐ 10%

   C ☐ 1%

   D ☐ 0.1%

6. There are 80 guests at a wedding reception. 30% of them do not eat meat.

   How many guests do not eat meat?

   A ☐ 24

   B ☐ 30

   C ☐ 50

   D ☐ 56

7. In an office, 75% of staff eat in the company's canteen.

   What fraction does not eat in the canteen?

   A ☐ $\frac{3}{4}$

   B ☐ $\frac{1}{4}$

   C ☐ $\frac{1}{3}$

   D ☐ $\frac{1}{2}$

8. Out of 444 people working at a local factory, 111 joined the union.

   What percentage of employees are in the union?

   A ☐ 25%

   B ☐ 4%

   C ☐ 20%

   D ☐ 44%

9. At a local cinema, 250 people attended the 8.30pm showing of a film. Of these people, 40% were senior citizens.

   How many people attending this film were senior citizens?

   A ☐ 40

   B ☐ 80

   C ☐ 100

   D ☐ 120

F Working with units and scales

You should already know how to:

✓ read, measure and record time

✓ read, measure and compare lengths, weights and capacities, using appropriate metric units

✓ read scales to the nearest division.

By the end of this section you will know how to:

▷▷ solve problems involving time, including reading timetables

▷▷ convert and calculate with metric units of length, weight and capacity

▷▷ work out which units of measurement to use

▷▷ use scales to find lengths and distances in real life and lengths on scale diagrams.

1 Time and timetables

⏸ **First read this …**

These are both ways of showing twenty past three in the afternoon:

3.20pm

15:20

15:20

This is 12-hour time or clock time

This is 24-hour time

▷ To convert from 12-hour time to 24-hour time:

  ▷ leave morning (am) times the same

  ▷ add 12 to afternoon (pm) times.

3pm ⟩ = 3 + 12 = ⟩ 15:00   7pm ⟩ = 7 + 12 = ⟩ 19:00

Tip

To convert from 24-hour clock, subtract 12 from times after 13:00:

20:00 ⟩ – 12 = ⟩ 8pm

17:00 ⟩ – 12 = ⟩ 5pm

Timetables can be used to plan journeys. You can use the timetable to work out what time you need to leave.

Example 1: Here is a timetable for trains travelling between Manchester Piccadilly and London Euston stations.

a What time does the 1032 train from Stockport arrive at London Euston, in standard clock time?

b A man is planning to catch a train from Macclesfield to London Euston. He needs to arrive in London at 2:30pm. He wants to leave Macclesfield as late as possible. Which train should he catch?

Manchester Piccadilly	1023	1123	1223	1323
Stockport ⟶	1032	1132	1232	1332
Macclesfield ⟶	1052	1152	1252	1352
Stoke-on-Trent	1112	1212	1312	1412
Milton Keynes	1220		1423	
Watford Junction		1340		1539
London Euston	1303	1403	1503	1603

a First find the 1032 train from Stockport. Then read down until you find the time that lines up with London Euston: 1303. Convert this to clock time: 1:03pm.

_____ Answer: 1:03pm _____

b Convert to 24-hour time: 2:30pm is 1430. He must arrive on the train that arrives at 1403. Read up the column to find the time this train leaves Macclesfield: 1152.

_____ Answer: 1152 _____

Tip

Some boxes in the timetable are blank because the train is not scheduled to stop there.

▶▶ Now try it!

1. The train timetable shows train times for the journey between London Liverpool Street and Silver Street.

   a At what time does the 0652 from Cambridge Heath arrive at Seven Sisters?

   _____

   b What is the latest train you can catch from Hackney Downs in order to arrive at Silver Street by 8:00am?

   _____

   c What is the latest train you can catch from London Liverpool Street in order to arrive at Seven Sisters by quarter past seven in the morning?

   _____

London Liverpool Street	0615	0628	0641	0654	0707
Cambridge Heath	0626	0639	0652	0705	0718
Hackney Downs	0632	0645	0658	0711	0724
Stoke Newington	0643	0656	0709	0722	0735
Seven Sisters	0657	0710	0723	0736	0749
Silver Street	0719	0732	0745	0758	0811

2. This timetable shows times of trains between Bournemouth and Edinburgh.

   a A woman wants to take a train from Bournemouth to Edinburgh. She leaves Bournemouth at ten to eight in the morning. What time will she arrive in Edinburgh?

   _____

   b A man needs to arrive in Glasgow by three o'clock in the afternoon. What time should he catch a train in Birmingham to do this?

   _____

Bournemouth	0550	0620	0750	0915
Birmingham	1018	1112	1218	1343
Glasgow	1443	1513	1643	1818
Edinburgh	1517	1643	1831	1948

First read this ...

You need to be able to work out how long something takes. A timeline can help.

Test tip

Test questions often involve how long a TV programme lasts or how long a journey will take.

Example 1: A lorry driver left central London at 9:30am and arrived in Oxford at 11:10am. How long did his journey take?

Sketch a timeline:

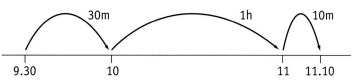

Count on from 9:30 to 10:00: 30 minutes
Between 10:00 and 11:00: 1 hour
Count on from 11:00 to 11:10: 10 minutes
Add the jumps: 30 minutes + 1 hour + 10 minutes
= 1 hour 40 minutes

Answer: 1 hour 40 minutes

Example 2: A chef knows it will take two hours and twenty minutes to prepare and cook an evening meal. He starts at 5:55pm. When will the meal be ready to serve?

Sketch a timeline:

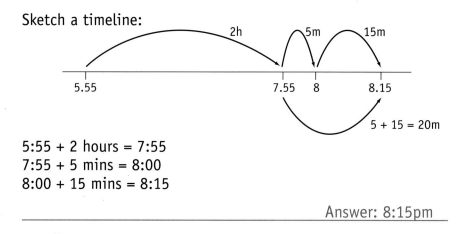

5:55 + 2 hours = 7:55
7:55 + 5 mins = 8:00
8:00 + 15 mins = 8:15

Answer: 8:15pm

Now try it!

1. Work out how much time has passed between each pair of start and stop times.

	Start	Stop	
a	9:10am	9:30am	*20*
b	8:15pm	10:25pm	*2 h 10m*
c	5:05am	11:40am	
d	10:30am	12:15pm	

2. Three friends went to a concert. They left home at 5:45pm and arrived at the concert venue at 7:25pm. How long did the journey take them?

_____

3. A video of a film starts at ten past seven in the evening and finishes later that evening at five to nine. How long does the film last?

_____

4. The table gives start and stop times, using the 24-hour clock. Work out how much time has passed in each case.

	Start	Stop	
a	1005	1215	
b	1120	1345	
c	0840	1410	
d	2330	0215	

5. A television programme starts at 1945 and finishes at 2210. How long is the programme, in hours and minutes?

_____

> **Remember**
>
> 1945 is in 24-hour time. This is the same as 7:45pm.

6. A train timetable shows that a train leaving Manchester Piccadilly at 1440 is due to arrive at London Euston at 1715. How long will this journey take?

_____

7. A man starts his afternoon shift at 1:35pm. The shift lasts for four and a quarter hours. What time will he finish?

_____

_____

8. A family plan to catch a ferry and need to book in at 11:30am. The journey to the ferry port will take 2 hours 45 minutes. What time should they leave home in order to get to the ferry port on time?

_____

_____

3 Length, weight and capacity

First read this ...

You should know the metric units and how to convert between them.

▷ To change from big units to small units, you **multiply**.

▷ To change from small units to big units, you **divide**.

Length

The metric units of length are metres (m), centimetres (cm) and millimetres (mm).

▷ 10 mm = 1 cm   ▷ 100 cm = 1 m

Example 1: Change:
a 560 mm to cm.   **b** 3.2 m to cm.

a You change from a small unit (mm) to a bigger unit (cm) so you divide.
$560 \div 10 = 56$ Answer: 56 cm

b You change from a big unit (m) to a smaller unit (cm) so you multiply.
$3.2 \times 100 = 320$ Answer: 320 cm

> **Tip**
>
> To change millimetres to centimetres, divide by 10.
> To change metres to centimetres, multiply by 100.

Weight

The metric units of weight are grams (g) and kilograms (kg).

▷ 1 000 g = 1 kg

Example 2: Which is the lighter weight, 4.5 kg or 4 kg 50 g?

First, change both amounts so they are in grams:
$4.5 \times 1 000 = 4 500$ so 4.5 kg = 4 500 g
4 kg = 4 000 g so 4 kg 50 g = 4 050 g
4 500 g is more than 4 050 g.   Answer: 4 kg 50 g is lighter.

> **Tip**
>
> To change kilograms to grams, multiply by 1 000.
> To change grams to kilograms, divide by 1 000.

Capacity

The metric units of capacity are litres (l) and millilitres (ml).

▷ 1 000 ml = 1 l

Example 3: Three bottles contain 75 ml, 750 ml and 1.75 litres of juice. Can all the juice be mixed in a 2.5 litre jug?

First, change the amount in litres into millilitres:
$1.75 \times 1 000 = 1 750$ so 1.75 litres = 1 750 ml

Now add the three amounts: $75 + 750 + 1 750 = 2 575$ ml
2 575 ml = 2.575 litres, which is more than 2.5 litres.

Answer: The juice cannot all be mixed in a 2.5 litre jug.

> **Tip**
>
> To convert from litres to millilitres, multiply by 1 000.
> To convert from millilitres to litres, divide by 1 000.

▶▶ *Now try it!*

1. Convert these lengths from metres into centimetres.

   a 5.4 m   b 0.25 m   c 2.25 m

   _____   _____   _____

Test tip

Check to make sure your answer makes sense:
5.4 m is about 5 m
5 m is 500 cm

2. Convert these lengths from centimetres into metres.

   a 250 cm   b 65 cm   c 3 cm

   _____   _____   _____

3. Convert these lengths from centimetres into millimetres.

   a 4 cm   b 2.5 cm   c 0.2 cm

   _____   _____   _____

4. Convert these lengths from millimetres into centimetres.

   a 50 mm   b 63 mm   c 3 mm

   _____   _____   _____

5. A tiling pattern uses three small tiles. The lengths of the tiles are 5.3 cm, 320 mm and 19 mm. What is their total length, in centimetres?

   _____

Test tip

Look at the units in the answer. Make sure the quantities are all in these units before you calculate.

6. Convert the following from kilograms into grams.

   a 5 kg   b 4.5 kg   c 2.25 kg

   _____   _____   _____

7. Convert these weights from grams into kilograms.

   a 5 000 g   b 600 g   c 350 g

   _____   _____   _____

8. A farmer sells three lambs. Their weights are 86.7 kg, 80 kg and 79 kg 75 g. What is their total weight?

   _____

9. Convert these capacities into millilitres.

   a 3 litres   b 2.6 litres   c 4.75 litres

   _____   _____   _____

10. Convert these capacities into litres.

    a 2 000 ml   b 3 500 ml   c 6 750 ml

    _____   _____   _____

11. Put these capacities in order, starting with the smallest.

    750 ml   0.075 litres   0.5 litres

    _____

4 Units and scales

First read this ...

The **metric units** for length, weight and capacity are the **metre**, the **gram** and the **litre**.

▷ **Length** has **one dimension**.

Length is measured in units such as kilometres (km), metres (m) or centimetres (cm).

▷ **Area** has **two dimensions** – **length** and **width**.

Area is measured in square units, such as square metres (m^2) or square centimetres (cm^2).

▷ **Volume** has **three dimensions** – **length**, **width** and **height**.

Volume is measured in cubic units, such as cubic metres (m^3).

You can work out which units are sensible to use, based on the size of an object and how many dimensions it has.

Example 1: A plumber needs a length of pipe to fit underneath a kitchen sink. What metric unit should she use?

Length has one dimension, so the choices are millimetres (mm), centimetres (cm), metres (m) or kilometres (km). Millimetres are very small, metres and kilometres are too big for a kitchen sink. So centimetres is the most sensible choice.

Answer: centimetres

A ruler is a scale for measuring length.
A metric ruler is marked in millimetres and centimetres.
The line ends between 3 cm and 4 cm, at the fourth small mark.

The line is 3 cm 4 mm or 3.4 cm long.

To read a scale you need to know what each mark is worth.

Example 2: What is the measurement indicated by the arrow?

This scale shows 100 ml to 200 ml.

There are five divisions between 100 ml and 200 ml.

100 ml ÷ 5 = 20 ml, so each division is worth 20 ml.

The arrow is pointing at the second mark: 100 + 40 = 140 ml

Answer: 140 ml

Test tip

kilo means 1 000
so 1 kilogram = 1 000 g
   1 kilometre = 1 000 m

Tip

A kilometre takes about 20 minutes to walk.

Tip

Carpet and wallpaper are sold in square metres (m^2).

Tip

Volume is the amount of space a solid takes up. Capacity is the maximum amount a container can hold. 1 litre is equivalent to 1000 cm^3.

Tip

There are 10 mm in 1 cm, so each small mark on the ruler counts as 1 mm.

▶▶ *Now try it!*

Use metric units for all these questions.

1. What unit would you use to measure:

   a the amount of milk in a container? _____

   b the weight of a suitcase? _____

   c your height? _____

   d the amount in a tin? _____

   e rope needed for climbing? _____

   f the amount of space inside a 4-wheel drive vehicle?

   _____

   g the distance between two towns, in real life?

   _____

2. A man measures the length, width and height of a cardboard box, in centimetres. He then calculates its volume. What units should he use?

   _____

3. Mark each of these measurements with an arrow on the ruler.

   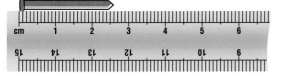

   a 30 mm   b 45 mm   c 3 mm   d 2 cm   e 1.3 cm   f 4.8 cm

4. These scales show weights, in kilograms. What weights are the arrows pointing to:

   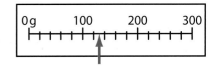

   a in kg _____

   b in kg and g? _____

5. This postal scale measures the weights of letters, in grams. What weight does the pointer show?

   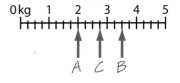

6. How long is this nail? _____

7. How much liquid is there in this measuring jug?

   _____

5 Using scales and scale diagrams

First read this ...

A map scale is 1 cm : 2 m. This means that 1 cm on a map or scale drawing **represents** 2 m in real life.

Actual measurements (such as length or distance) can be worked out from **scales** on **maps** or **scale diagrams**.

Example 1: Study the scale diagram of a sports hall. Work out the length of the sports hall.

The sports hall measures 6 cm on the plan.

The scale is given as 1 cm : 2 m. This means 1 cm on the plan represents 2 m in real life.

To find the real length of the hall, multiply the length on the plan by 2:

6 cm on plan → 6 × 2 m = 12 m

Answer: 12 m

The scale 2 cm : 1 m means that every 2 cm on a map or scale drawing represents 1 metre in real life.

Example 2: The scale on an architect's plan is 2 cm : 1 m. The actual length of a room is 5 m. What is the length of the room on the plan?

The room is 5 m long.
The scale is given as 2 cm : 1 m.
This means 2 cm on the plan equals 1 m in real life.
To find the length of the room on the plan, multiply the length by 2: 5 m → 5 × 2 = 10 cm

Answer: 10 cm

> **Tip**
>
> 1 cm : 2 m means 1 cm for every 2 m.

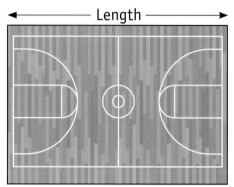

Length

1 cm : 2 m

Now try it!

1. Use the scale given to work out the actual length for each of these map lengths.

	Scale	Map length	Actual length
a	1 cm : 5 m	3 cm	
b	1 cm : 10 m	5.5 cm	
c	1 cm : 2.5 km	8 cm	
d	1 cm : 2 m	30 mm	
e	1 cm : 4 m	40 mm	

> **Tip**
>
> The scale gives the number of metres or kilometres for every 1 centimetre, so multiply the number of centimetres on your drawing by this number.

2. A woman is planning a bike ride. She uses a map with a scale of 1 cm : 5 km. The distance she wants to cycle is 7.8 cm on the map. How many kilometres is this?

_____

3. On a scale drawing, a garden path is 16 cm long. The scale is given as 4 cm : 1 m. How long is the path in reality?

_____

4. On the plan of a nursery, a child's playpen is 3 cm wide. The scale of the drawing is 2 cm to 1 m. How wide is the playpen, in metres?

_____

5. A rambler uses a map with a scale of 5 cm to 1 km. On the map, the distance between two landmarks is 30 cm. What is the actual distance between the two landmarks?

_____

6. A builder draws a plan for a house, using the scale 1 cm : 2 m. The house is 8.2 m wide. What is the width of the house on the plan?

_____

7. What distance, on a map with a scale of 5 cm to 1 km, would represent an actual distance of 15 kilometres?

_____

8. The organiser of a sponsored 18 km run draws a plan diagram of the race, to a scale of 1 cm : 4 km. What length will the line showing the race route be?

_____

9. Two friends are planning to go on a walk that is 8 km long. The scale on their map is 2 cm to 1 km. How far is 8 km on the map?

_____

10. A couple use a map with a scale of 1 cm to 5 km to plan a kayak trip. They draw a line showing their 40 km trip on the map. How long is the line they draw on the map?

_____

First complete this ...

▷ To change from big units to small units, you _____.

▷ To change from small units to big units, you _____.

▷ 10 mm = 1 ___   ▷ 100 cm = 1 ___

▷ 1 000 g = 1 ___   ▷ 1 000 ml = 1 ___

▷ _____ has one dimension.

▷ _____ has two dimensions – length and width.

▷ _____ has three dimensions – length, width and height.

> **Test tip**
>
> Learn the relationships between these units and write them down as soon as the test starts. For example, write down 1 000 ml = 1 litre.

Now try it!

1. A man uses a map that has a scale of 2 centimetres to 1 kilometre to plan a walk. The distance he wants to walk on the map is 24 cm long.

   How far is the actual walk?

   A ☐ 48 km

   B ☐ 24 km

   C ☐ 12 km

   D ☐ 6 km

2. A film starts at 2050 and finishes at 2205.

   How long, in hours and minutes, does the film last?

   A ☐ 1 hour 15 minutes

   B ☐ 1 hour 45 minutes

   C ☐ 1 hour 55 minutes

   D ☐ 2 hours 15 minutes

3. The map shows the position of the hall and shop in a village.

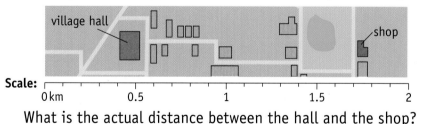

   Scale:

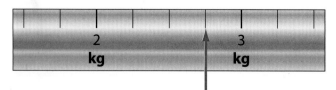

   0 km   0.5   1   1.5   2

   What is the actual distance between the hall and the shop?

   A ☐ 0.8 km

   B ☐ 1 km

   C ☐ 1.2 km

   D ☐ 1.5 km

4. What weight is the arrow indicating?

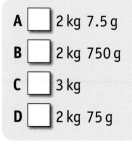

   A ☐ 2 kg 7.5 g

   B ☐ 2 kg 750 g

   C ☐ 3 kg

   D ☐ 2 kg 75 g

5. The table shows the weights of four parcels ready for posting.

2 kg 500 g	1 kg 250 g	750 g	1 kg 50 g

What is the total weight of the four parcels?

A ☐ 4 kg 550 g

B ☐ 6 kg

C ☐ 5 kg 550 g

D ☐ 5 kg

6. A woman has an interview at 2pm. She needs 1 hour 45 minutes travel time.

What is the latest time she could leave home?

A ☐ 11:15am

B ☐ 11:55am

C ☐ 12:15pm

D ☐ 12:45pm

7. Which units are likely to be used to measure medicine?

A ☐ square cm

B ☐ litres

C ☐ grams

D ☐ millilitres

8. A field is 40 metres long. A man makes a scale diagram of the field, using a scale of 1 mm : 1 m.

What will be the length of the field on his drawing?

A ☐ 4 cm

B ☐ 4 mm

C ☐ 4 m

D ☐ 40 cm

9. The timetable shows the times of trains from Manchester Piccadilly to Chester.

Manchester Piccadilly	1333	1358	1428	1445
Chester	1428	1453	1523	1540

A man arrives at Manchester Piccadilly station at a quarter to two in the afternoon and catches the next train. What time will he arrive in Chester?

A ☐ 1428

B ☐ 1453

C ☐ 1523

D ☐ 1540

10. The diagram shows the amount of fuel in a storage tank.

How much fuel is there in the tank?

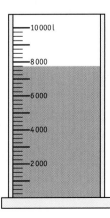

A ☐ 7500 litres

B ☐ 8000 litres

C ☐ 7750 litres

D ☐ 6750 litres

G Working with perimeter, area and volume

You should already know how to:

✓ read, measure and compare metric units of length.

By the end of this section you will know how to:

▷ calculate the perimeter of a shape

▷ estimate and calculate the area of a rectangular shape

▷ calculate the volume of a cuboid

▷ use the correct units of measurement for area and volume.

1 Calculating perimeter and area

First read this ...

▷ The **perimeter** of a shape is the distance all the way around its boundary.

Example 1: What is the perimeter of the shape?

Add up the lengths of all the sides: 8 + 3 + 8 + 3 = 22 cm

Answer: 22 cm

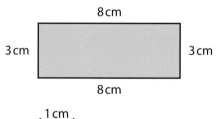

▷ **Area** is the amount of space taken up by a shape.

The rectangle is made up of eight unit squares.
Each unit square measures 1 cm by 1 cm and its area is 1 cm².
The area of the rectangle is 8 cm².

There are 4 columns and 2 rows: 4 × 2 = 8 cm²

▷ The **area** of a rectangle = **length × width**.

Example 2: A rectangular garden is 9.8 metres wide and 20 metres long. What is the area of the garden?

First, identify the length (20 m) and the width (9.8 m).
To find the area, multiply length and width:

9.8 × 20 m² = 9.8 × 2 × 10 m² = 19.6 × 10 m² = 196 m²

Answer: 196 m²

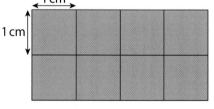

Tip

Area is measured in **two dimensions**, so it is always measured in **square units**, such as mm², cm² or m².

Remember

To multiply a number by 20, multiply first by 2 and then multiply the result by 10.

Now try it!

1. Work out the perimeters of the following shapes.

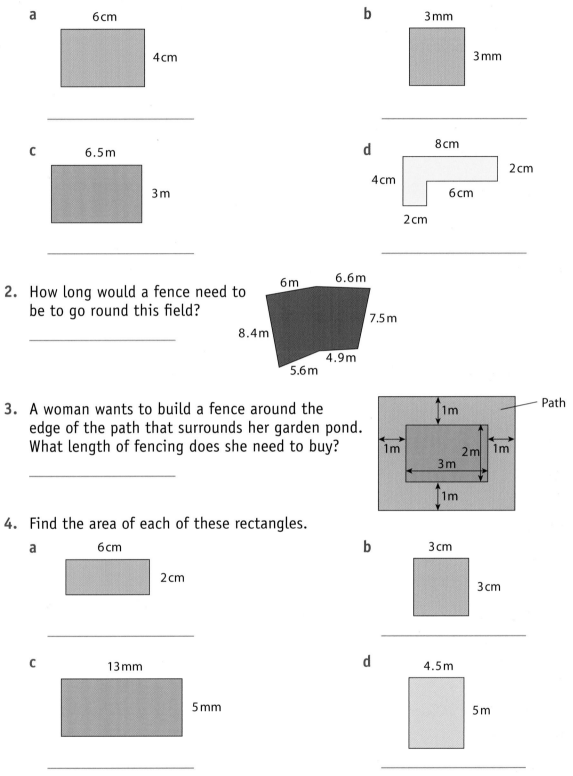

   a 6cm / 4cm

   b 3mm / 3mm

   c 6.5m / 3m

   d 8cm / 2cm / 4cm / 6cm / 2cm

2. How long would a fence need to be to go round this field?

   _____

   6m 6.6m 7.5m 8.4m 4.9m 5.6m

3. A woman wants to build a fence around the edge of the path that surrounds her garden pond. What length of fencing does she need to buy?

   _____

   Path 1m 1m 2m 1m 3m 1m

4. Find the area of each of these rectangles.

   a 6cm / 2cm

   b 3cm / 3cm

   c 13mm / 5mm

   d 4.5m / 5m

5. A window is 50 centimetres wide and 2 metres long. What is its area?

   _____

6. A corridor has a rectangular floor of length 8 metres and width 1.5 metres. Find its area.

   _____

2 Area and volume

First read this ...

You can work out the **approximate area** of a shape using **estimates**.

> **Example 1:** A gardener wants to reseed a client's lawn. The lawn is a rectangle 18.75 metres long and 8.59 metres wide. What calculation can he do to work out the area of the lawn roughly?

First, round the length and width to the nearest whole numbers.

18.75 rounds up to 19, and 8.59 rounds up to 9.

Area is calculated by multiplying length and width.

Answer: 19 × 9

▷ **Volume** is the amount of space taken up by a three-dimensional (3-D) solid.

In this cuboid there are 6 (= 3 × 2) cubes.

Each cube measures 1 cm by 1 cm by 1 cm so its volume is 1 cm³.

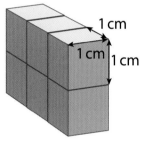

The volume of the cuboid is 6 cm³: 3 × 2 × 1 = 6 cm³.

▷ The **volume** of a cuboid = **length** × **width** × **height**.

> **Example 2:** A box has length 5 cm, width 2 cm and height 4 cm. What is its volume?

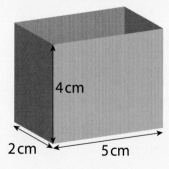

First, identify the length (5 cm), the width (2 cm), and the height (4 cm).

Volume = length × width × height

5 × 2 × 4 = 40cm³

Answer: 40 cm³

Remember

Round up when the key digit is 5 or more.

Tip

Volume is measured in **three dimensions**, so it is always measured in **cubic units**: cubic millimetres (mm³), cubic centimetres (cm³) or cubic metres (m³).

Tip

A cuboid is the mathematical name for a box. A cube is a special type of cuboid: its sides are all the same length.

▶▶ *Now try it!*

1. A carpet layer is ordering new carpet for a living room. The floor of the room is 5.92 metres long and 3.74 metres wide. Which two numbers should he multiply together to work out an approximate area of the floor?

   _____

2. The front of a house is being repainted. The front is rectangular in shape and is 12.78 m wide and 14.8 m high. What is the approximate area that will be repainted?

   _____

3. Find the volume of these cuboids.

   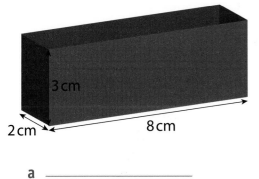   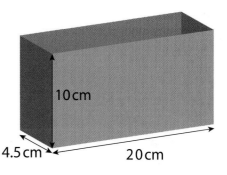

   a _____   b _____

4. An ice cube has length, width and height of 3 cm. What is its volume?

   _____

5. The dimensions of a room are:
   length 8 metres, width 5.5 metres, height 3 metres.
   What is the volume of the room?

   _____

6. A brick is 15 cm in length, 10 cm in width and 2.5 cm in depth. What is its volume?

   _____

7. A fish tank is 20 cm wide, 30 cm long and 40 cm high. How much water can it hold when it is full to the top?

   _____

8. A tall city building is 160 m high, 20 m long and 15 m wide. What is the volume of the building?

   _____

First complete this ...

▷ The _____ of a shape is the distance all the way around its boundary.

▷ _____ is the amount of space taken up by a shape.

▷ The area of a rectangle = _____ × _____.

▷ _____ is the amount of space taken up by a three-dimensional (3-D) solid.

▷ The volume of a cuboid = _____ × _____ × _____.

Test tip

If a question gives dimensions in different units, convert them so that all the units are the same before you work out perimeter, area or volume.

Now try it!

1. A rugby pitch measures 200 metres long and 90 metres wide.

   What is the area of the pitch?

   A ☐ 290 m²

   B ☐ 18 000 m²

   C ☐ 380 m²

   D ☐ 1 800 m²

2. A woman wants to gravel over her garden. She estimates the garden to be 8.4 metres long by 7.5 metres wide.

   What is the approximate area of her garden?

   A ☐ 64 m²

   B ☐ 56 m²

   C ☐ 58 m²

   D ☐ 70 m²

3. In a house, the kitchen floor is 6 metres long by 5 metres wide. The floor area is calculated to be 30 units.

   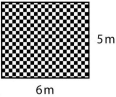
   5 m
   6 m

   What is the unit for the floor area?

   A ☐ m

   B ☐ m²

   C ☐ m³

   D ☐ cm

4. This diagram shows a water container.

   How much water does the container hold when it is full?

   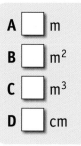
   25 cm
   10 cm   20 cm

   A ☐ 55 cm³

   B ☐ 500 cm³

   C ☐ 755 cm³

   D ☐ 5 000 cm³

5. How long would a fence need to be in order to enclose this boating lake?

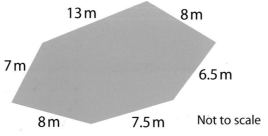

13 m   8 m

7 m

6.5 m

8 m   7.5 m   Not to scale

A ☐ 50 m

B ☐ 60 m

C ☐ 80 m

D ☐ 100 m

6. A man wants to put new carpet on the floor in his office. The floor is 6.92 metres long and 4.84 metres wide.

Which of the following calculations should he use to find a quick estimate of the area of the floor?

A ☐ 6 × 4

B ☐ 6 × 5

C ☐ 7 × 4

D ☐ 7 × 5

7. The diagram shows a cardboard box used to package perfume. The box is a cube of side length 10 cm.

What is its volume?

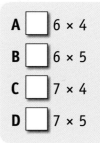

A ☐ 1 000 cm²

B ☐ 100 cm³

C ☐ 100 cm²

D ☐ 1 000 cm³

8. A rectangular area in a garden is to be paved for a patio.

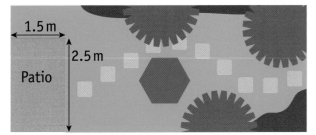

1.5 m

2.5 m

Patio

What is the area to be paved for the patio?

A ☐ 1.25 m²

B ☐ 3.50 m²

C ☐ 3.75 m²

D ☐ 4.00 m²

9. How do you work out the correct volume of this box?

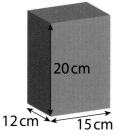

20 cm

12 cm   15 cm

A ☐ Add 12, 15 and 20 together.

B ☐ Add 12, 15 and 20 together, then multiply by 2.

C ☐ Add 20 to 15, then multiply by 12.

D ☐ Multiply 20 by 15 by 12.

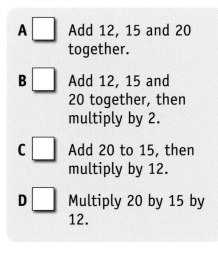

H Working with data

You should already know:

✓ how to present data in simple tables, bar charts, pie charts and pictograms and include appropriate information

✓ how to interpret bar charts and pictograms

✓ what tally marks mean and how to use them.

By the end of this section, you will know how to:

▷ interpret data in tables, charts and graphs

▷ use mileage charts

▷ interpret tally marks in order to solve problems

▷ identify essential features of bar charts, line graphs, pie charts and pictograms.

1 Interpreting tables and recording data

First read this ...

You need to be able to read the information in a table in order to solve a problem.

Example 1: The table shows the cost of a two-week skiing trip in different countries.

How much will a two-week skiing trip to Italy on half-board basis cost?

Country	SC	BB	HB
Austria	£245	£205	£189
Bulgaria	£202	£302	£253
France	£149	£258	£149
Italy	£199	£214	£209
Norway	£259	–	£413

Key: SC self-catering; BB bed and breakfast; HB half-board

Tip

Use a ruler or piece of paper with a straight edge to read across the row correctly.

First, use the key to find out how half-board is shown in the table: in this case it is shown by HB, so you only need to look at the data in this column.

Now find Italy and read across this row to find the HB value.

Answer: £209

Mileage charts show the distance in miles between cities.

Example 2: Use the mileage chart to work out the distance from Birmingham to Exeter.

First, find the column for Birmingham.

Then read down this column to the row for Exeter.

The value in this cell shows the distance between these cities.

Answer: 164 miles

Birmingham	Edinburgh	Exeter	Liverpool
298			
164	454		
102	224	258	

When you collect information, you need a way to record and organise it.

Tally marks are easy to use and quick to count.

Example 3: Three traffic surveyors record the number of vehicles entering a danger zone in 10 minutes. How many more vehicles did Surveyor C record than Surveyor A?

Surveyor A	ЦЦ ///
Surveyor B	ЦЦ //
Surveyor C	ЦЦ ЦЦ

Each ЦЦ group of tallies counts as 5.

So, Surveyor C recorded 10, and Surveyor A recorded 8.

Answer: 2 vehicles

Tip

Groups of tallies are easy to count because they represent groups of 5.

▶▶ *Now try it!*

1. Here is part of a catalogue featuring digital cameras.

   a What is the price of the camera that has four megapixels and a 4× zoom? _____

   b What is the catalogue number of the camera that has a 3× zoom and has four megapixels?

   _____

Item number	Catalogue number	Megapixels	Zoom	Price
1	680/453	3.5	3×	£69.75
2	680/454	4	3×	£79.75
3	680/455	4	4×	£99.99
4	680/456	5	4×	£109.25

2. A couple going on a three-week holiday to Europe are planning to buy holiday insurance. Use the table to answer this question.

   a How much will they pay for their insurance? _____

   b How much extra will the insurance cost them if they take their young son? _____

Insurance	Adult	Couple	Family
Europe 1 week (up to 8 days)	£15	£24	£40
Europe 2 weeks (up to 15 days)	£25	£45	£50
Europe 1 year	£30	£55	£75
Worldwide 1 week (up to 8 days)	£30	£48	£70

2 Bar charts and pie charts

First read this ...

▷ A bar chart uses bars to show patterns in data.

This bar chart shows the meals chosen in a canteen one lunchtime.

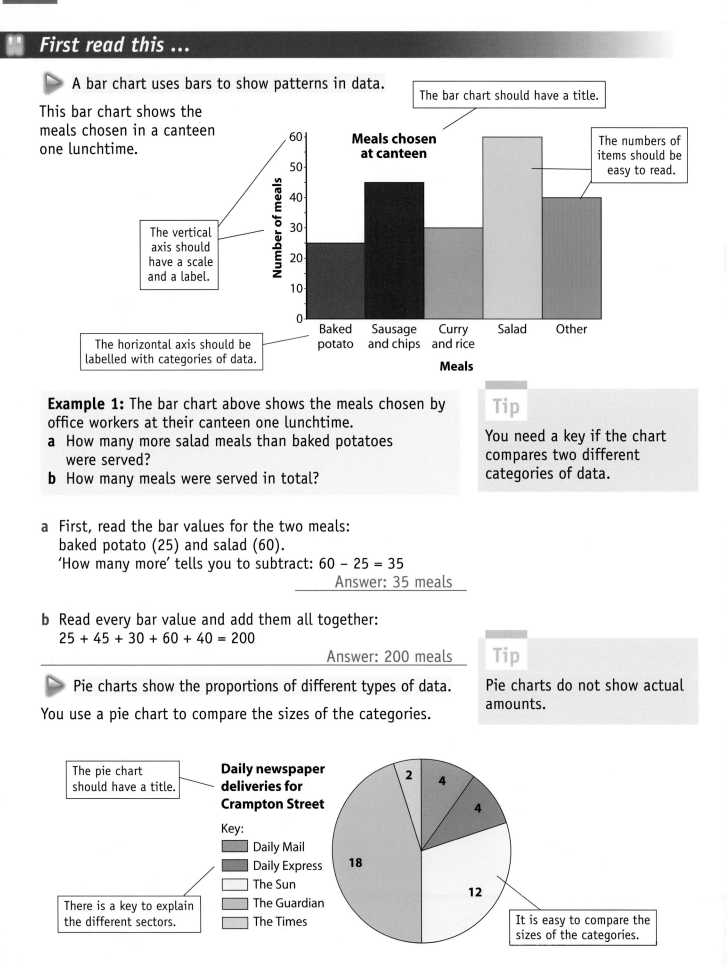

The bar chart should have a title.

The numbers of items should be easy to read.

The vertical axis should have a scale and a label.

The horizontal axis should be labelled with categories of data.

Example 1: The bar chart above shows the meals chosen by office workers at their canteen one lunchtime.
a How many more salad meals than baked potatoes were served?
b How many meals were served in total?

Tip

You need a key if the chart compares two different categories of data.

a First, read the bar values for the two meals:
baked potato (25) and salad (60).
'How many more' tells you to subtract: 60 − 25 = 35

Answer: 35 meals

b Read every bar value and add them all together:
25 + 45 + 30 + 60 + 40 = 200

Answer: 200 meals

▷ Pie charts show the proportions of different types of data.

You use a pie chart to compare the sizes of the categories.

Tip

Pie charts do not show actual amounts.

The pie chart should have a title.

Daily newspaper deliveries for Crampton Street

Key:
- Daily Mail
- Daily Express
- The Sun
- The Guardian
- The Times

There is a key to explain the different sectors.

It is easy to compare the sizes of the categories.

Example 2: The pie chart shows the daily newspaper deliveries for Crampton Street.

a Which is the least popular newspaper?

b Which newspaper accounts for roughly half of the deliveries?

a The least popular choice is shown by the smallest sector: pink. Use the key to work out which newspaper this is.

Answer: The Times

b The green sector takes up about half of the pie chart. Use the key to find out which newspaper this is.

Answer: The Guardian

▶ *Now try it!*

1. A Saturday afternoon TV sports programme showed four sports. The bar chart shows the number of hours given to each sport in the programme.

   a How long was the programme, in total?

   _____

   b Which sports were given the same viewing time?

   _____

   c How many more hours were given to football than cricket?

   _____

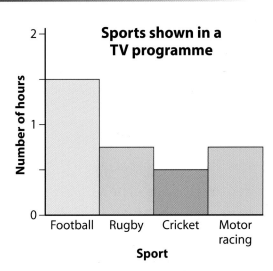

2. The pie chart shows the weather in a UK city for the month of February.

   a Ring each of the statements that is true.

   A A quarter of the days were cloudy.

   B There were twice as many rainy days as sunny.

   C A third of the days were sunny.

   b Which type of weather was roughly twice as common as snow?

   _____

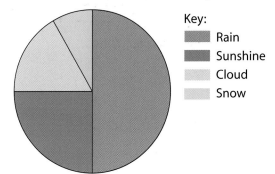

3. A shopkeeper recorded how many items she sold each day over a five-day period. She presented her sale figures on this bar chart. What is missing from the bar chart?

   _____

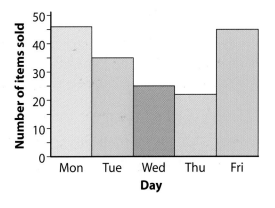

First read this ...

▷ Pictograms use pictures to show patterns in data.

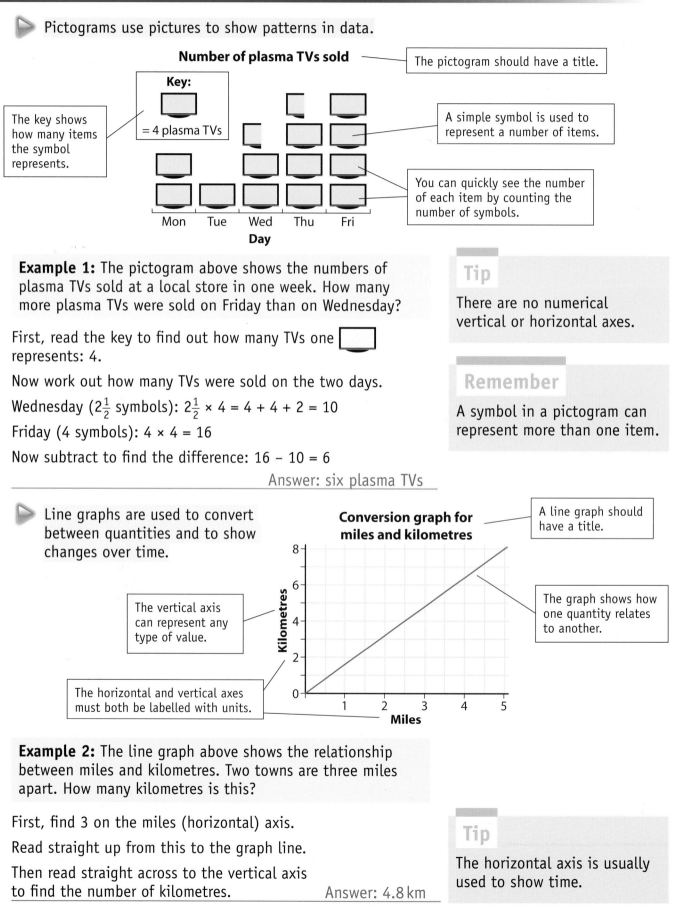

Number of plasma TVs sold

The pictogram should have a title.

Key:

= 4 plasma TVs

The key shows how many items the symbol represents.

A simple symbol is used to represent a number of items.

You can quickly see the number of each item by counting the number of symbols.

Mon   Tue   Wed   Thu   Fri
Day

Example 1: The pictogram above shows the numbers of plasma TVs sold at a local store in one week. How many more plasma TVs were sold on Friday than on Wednesday?

First, read the key to find out how many TVs one ⬚ represents: 4.

Now work out how many TVs were sold on the two days.

Wednesday ($2\frac{1}{2}$ symbols): $2\frac{1}{2} \times 4 = 4 + 4 + 2 = 10$

Friday (4 symbols): $4 \times 4 = 16$

Now subtract to find the difference: $16 - 10 = 6$

Answer: six plasma TVs

Tip

There are no numerical vertical or horizontal axes.

Remember

A symbol in a pictogram can represent more than one item.

▷ Line graphs are used to convert between quantities and to show changes over time.

Conversion graph for miles and kilometres

A line graph should have a title.

The vertical axis can represent any type of value.

The graph shows how one quantity relates to another.

The horizontal and vertical axes must both be labelled with units.

Example 2: The line graph above shows the relationship between miles and kilometres. Two towns are three miles apart. How many kilometres is this?

First, find 3 on the miles (horizontal) axis.

Read straight up from this to the graph line.

Then read straight across to the vertical axis to find the number of kilometres.

Answer: 4.8 km

Tip

The horizontal axis is usually used to show time.

▶ *Now try it!*

1. The pictogram shows the number of homes rented out in one month by a letting agent.

   Number of homes let

   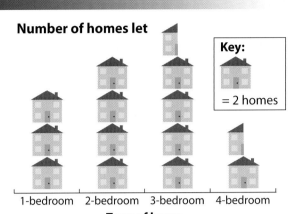

   Key:

    = 2 homes

   1-bedroom   2-bedroom   3-bedroom   4-bedroom
   Type of home

   a How many 3-bedroom homes were let that month?

   _____

   b How many more 2-bedroom homes were let than 4-bedroom homes?

   _____

2. The line graph shows the temperature in an oven from two to seven minutes after it is switched on.

   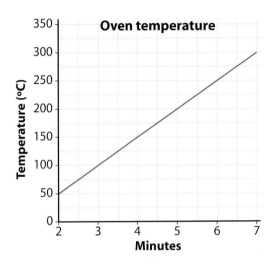

   a What is the temperature in the oven after $3\frac{1}{2}$ minutes?

   _____

   b How long does it take the oven to reach 150°C?

   _____

   c How much does the temperature increase between four and six minutes after the oven is switched on?

   _____

3. The pictogram shows the number of mobile phones sold at a shop over three weekends. What is missing from the pictogram?

   _____

   Number of mobile phones sold

   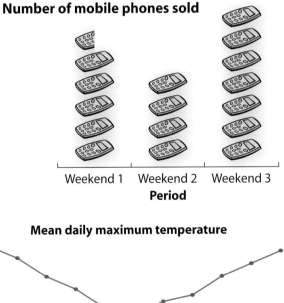

   Weekend 1   Weekend 2   Weekend 3
   Period

4. A holiday brochure shows the typical temperatures in Sydney. What is missing from the graph?

   _____

   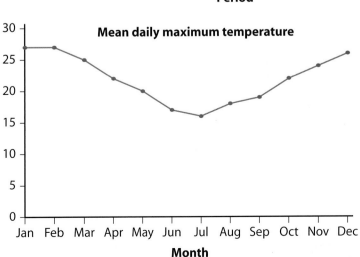

First complete this ...

▷ A _____ _____ uses bars to show patterns in data.

▷ _____ _____ show the proportions of different types of data.

▷ _____ use pictures to show patterns in data.

▷ _____ _____ are used to convert between quantities and to show changes over time.

Now try it!

1. A manager records the times deliveries are made to his depot. This chart shows the results.

   How many deliveries are made between 9:00 and 11:00?

   A ☐ 15
   B ☐ 40
   C ☐ 50
   D ☐ 70

2. The chart shows the numbers of people who went on four rides at a theme park one Thursday morning.

   What is missing from the chart?

   A ☐ Scale for the number of people
   B ☐ Title
   C ☐ Labels to show what the bars mean
   D ☐ Label for the vertical axis

3. The pictogram shows the numbers of calculators sold in one day at an electronics shop.

   How many Casio calculators were sold that day?

   A ☐ 9
   B ☐ 15
   C ☐ 17
   D ☐ 18

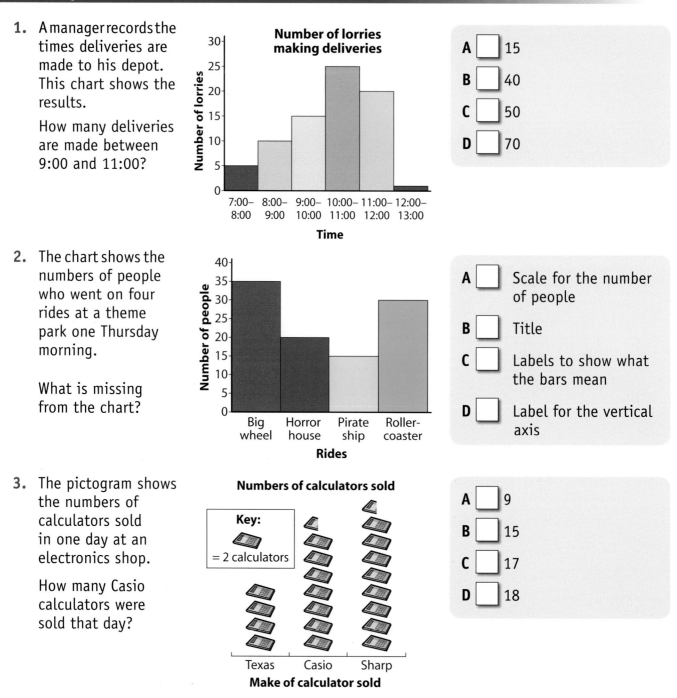

4. A nurse measures, records and plots a patient's temperature and draws this graph.

What is missing from the graph?

Patient's temperature readings

Temperature

40
39
38
37
36
35

08:00 10:00 12:00 14:00 16:00 18:00 20:00
Time of day

A	☐	A key for the chart
B	☐	A label for the vertical axis
C	☐	A label for the horizontal axis
D	☐	Units for the vertical axis

5. A builder uses the line graph to find the price of the wood according to the number of metres a customer wants.

How much will 2.5 metres of wood cost?

Price of wood per metre

Price of wood (£)

15

10

5

0

0   1   2   3   4   5
Number of metres

A	☐	£2.80
B	☐	£5.60
C	☐	£7.00
D	☐	£8.40

6. The manager of a day care centre keeps a tally chart of how many people attend each day. Each session can take up to 24 people.

Number of people attending the day care centre

	Morning session	Afternoon session
Mon	ℋℋ ℋℋ ℋℋ ℋℋ ///	ℋℋ ℋℋ ////
Tues	ℋℋ ℋℋ ℋℋ ///	ℋℋ ℋℋ ℋℋ //
Weds	ℋℋ ℋℋ ℋℋ ℋℋ ////	ℋℋ ℋℋ /
Thur	ℋℋ ℋℋ ///	ℋℋ ℋℋ
Fri	ℋℋ ℋℋ ℋℋ /	ℋℋ ℋℋ

How many more patients can the manager accept on a Tuesday morning session?

A	☐	0
B	☐	6
C	☐	7
D	☐	18

7. The mileage chart shows the distances in miles between different cities.

How far is Manchester from Exeter?

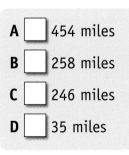

Edinburgh	Exeter	Liverpool	Manchester
454			
224	258		
219	246	35	

A	☐	454 miles
B	☐	258 miles
C	☐	246 miles
D	☐	35 miles

Working with mean and range

 You should already know how to:

✔ add, subtract and divide numbers with up to two places of decimals.

By the end of this section you will know how to:

▷▷ calculate the mean of up to ten items of data
▷▷ calculate the range of up to ten items of data.

1 Understanding the mean

First read this ...

The **mean** of a group of values is the value that is **typical** of the whole group.

▷ To calculate the mean:

  ▷ add up all the values

  ▷ divide by the number of values.

> **Tip**
>
> The mean is a kind of average.

Example 1: Find the mean of these values: 2, 11, 8, 6, 3.

First, add the values: 2 + 11 + 8 + 6 + 3 = 30
Then divide the total by the number of values:

30 ÷ 5 = 6   Answer: 6

Example 2: Find the mean of these temperatures recorded at noon over five days.

Monday	Tuesday	Wednesday	Thursday	Friday
5°C	3°C	3°C	0°C	2°C

Add the values: 5 + 3 + 3 + 0 + 2 = 13
Divide the total by the number of values:

13 ÷ 5 = 2.6   Answer: 2.6°C

Now try it!

1. Find the mean of each of these sets of values.

  a 12, 4, 14, 3, 7 _____

  b 5 cm, 4 cm, 0 cm, 2 cm, 2 cm,
     8 cm, 3 cm, 4 cm, 4 cm, 5 cm _____

  c £2.50, £1.24, £1.22, £1.60 _____

2. To help her budget, a trainee chef made a record of how much she spent each week for four weeks. What is the mean amount she spent per week?

Week 1	Week 2	Week 3	Week 4
£48	£50	£32	£20

Remember
You don't write the pence sign when writing amounts with the £ sign.

3. The table below shows the average number of hours of sunshine each day in the Algarve for the months of January to September.

Jan	Feb	Mar	Apr	May	Jun	Jul	Aug	Sep
5	7	8	9	10	11	12	10	9

What is the mean number of daily hours of sunshine for the months shown?

4. A parent researched the price of eight different drinks for children, four fizzy drinks and four fruit juices. His aim was to find out whether it is cheaper to buy fizzy drinks or fruit juices, on average.

Fruit juice	Price per 300 ml	Fizzy drink	Price per 300 ml
A	45p	A	55p
B	65p	B	85p
C	70p	C	50p
D	60p	D	60p

a What is the mean price of fruit juice per 300 ml?

b What is the mean price of fizzy drink per 300 ml?

c Which drink is more expensive, on average?

5. A cosmetics company offers a bonus to the sales team with the highest average weekly sales. Which team will win, based on the results of the first five weeks?

	Week 1	Week 2	Week 3	Week 4	Week 5
Team A sales (£)	1 067	1 258	2 164	1 775	2 234
Team B sales (£)	1 578	987	2 430	1 855	2 032

2 Mean and range

To find the mean you need to decide which number to divide by.

Example 1: A gardener plants 40 bulbs in one hour. What is the mean time taken to plant one bulb?

To find the mean time taken to plant one bulb, divide the total time by the number of bulbs.

$60 \div 40 = 1.5$ minutes   Answer: 1.5 minutes

Example 2: In one day, a taxi driver takes 50 passengers and drives a total of 200 miles. What is the mean distance per journey?

Total distance: 200 miles

To find the mean distance travelled per journey, divide the total distance by the number of passengers.

$200 \div 50 = 4$ miles   Answer: 4 miles

The **range** of a set of data tells you how widely the numbers are spread.

▷ The range = the **biggest value** – the **smallest value**.

Example 3: Find the range of these numbers:
5, 7, 2, 8, 8, 6, 12, 3.

The biggest value is: 12

The smallest value is: 2

The range is the difference: $12 - 2 = 10$ Answer: 10

Example 4: The temperature outside a glasshouse was recorded daily at 9:00am over five days. The results are given in the table below. What is the range?

Monday	Tuesday	Wednesday	Thursday	Friday
4°C	1°C	0°C	2°C	2°C

The highest temperature is 4°C.

The lowest temperature is 0°C.

The range is the difference: $4 - 0 = 4$ Answer: 4°C

Test tip

Check to make sure your answer is sensible. 1.5 mins for 1 bulb means:
3 mins for 2 bulbs
30 mins for 20 bulbs
60 mins for 40 bulbs

Tip

'What is the mean distance' is the key to the question.

Tip

The range also identifies how far apart the extremes in a set of data are.

Remember

To find the difference, you subtract.

Now try it!

1. A worker in a call centre takes 15 calls in 30 minutes. What is the mean time she takes to answer each call?

   _____

   Tip

   Find the total time and then divide by the number of calls.

2. A lorry makes 40 deliveries and travels a total of 400 miles. How many miles, on average, is each delivery?

   _____

3. In the first round of a football competition, 20 teams score a total of 50 goals. What is the average number of goals scored by each team?

   _____

   Tip

   To find the **average number of goals**, find the **total number** of goals first (50) and then divide this by the **number of teams** (20).

4. A market stall holder works for 20 hours and makes £450 in total. On average, how much does he make per hour?

   _____

5. A car uses five litres of petrol to travel 40 miles. What is the mean distance the car travels on one litre of petrol?

   _____

6. A computer technician takes 15 hours to install a new program on 20 computers. What is the mean length of time it takes her to install the program on one computer?

   _____

   Test tip

   Always check that your answer makes sense.

7. Find the range of each of these data sets.

   a 9, 13, 1, 8, 2, 3

   _____

   b 14°C, 0°C, 1°C, 15°C, 7°C

   _____

   c £3.00, £1.20, £4.50, £6.30, £2.00, £9.10

   _____

8. The table shows how many cars a salesman sold each month, over a six-month period.

April	May	June	July	August	September
12	10	6	12	6	8

   What is the range of the numbers of vehicles he has sold from April to September?

   _____

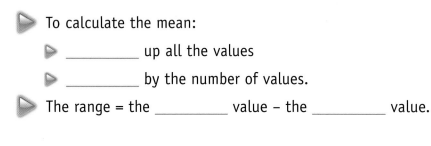

First complete this ...

▷ To calculate the mean:

   ▷ _____ up all the values

   ▷ _____ by the number of values.

▷ The range = the _____ value – the _____ value.

Test tip

Most questions on this topic give a table of data and require you to add the items and then divide by the number of items to find the mean.

Now try it!

1. The temperature in a health clinic was measured and recorded every day, at 9:00am, from Monday to Friday. The results are shown in the table.

Mon	Tues	Weds	Thurs	Fri
19°C	19°C	23°C	21°C	28°C

What was the mean daily temperature at 9:00am in the clinic over these five days?

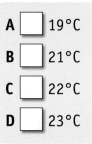

A ☐ 19°C

B ☐ 21°C

C ☐ 22°C

D ☐ 23°C

2. In five days an estate agent sold 25 houses.

How many did she sell per day, on average?

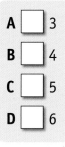

A ☐ 3

B ☐ 4

C ☐ 5

D ☐ 6

3. A dentist used this table to record the numbers of patients seen in a week. Use the table to answer questions 3 and 4.

Mon	Tues	Weds	Thurs	Fri
20	15	18	16	15

What is the range of the numbers of patients seen by the dentist?

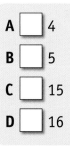

A ☐ 4

B ☐ 5

C ☐ 15

D ☐ 16

4. Use the data in question 3 to answer this question.

Which calculation gives the mean number of patients seen each day by the dentist over these five days?

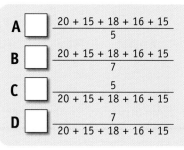

A ☐ $\dfrac{20 + 15 + 18 + 16 + 15}{5}$

B ☐ $\dfrac{20 + 15 + 18 + 16 + 15}{7}$

C ☐ $\dfrac{5}{20 + 15 + 18 + 16 + 15}$

D ☐ $\dfrac{7}{20 + 15 + 18 + 16 + 15}$

5. The table shows the amounts of money a man withdrew from a cash machine over five days.

Mon	Tues	Weds	Thurs	Fri
£20	£50	£0	£20	£100

What is the range of the amounts he withdrew over this period?

A ☐ £20
B ☐ £50
C ☐ £95
D ☐ £100

6. A woman is training for a race. She records the number of minutes she runs each day for one week, as shown in the table.

Mon	Tues	Weds	Thurs	Fri	Sat	Sun
44	41	41	45	41	40	42

What is the mean amount of time she spends running each day?

A ☐ 40 minutes
B ☐ 41 minutes
C ☐ 42 minutes
D ☐ 45 minutes

7. Five friends took part in a sponsored run and recorded the amounts they collected in the table shown.

Runner	Amount
Ali	£10.00
David	£24.00
Mel	£23.50
Nuala	£42.50
Shazira	£60.00

What is the mean amount of sponsorship money collected per person?

A ☐ £30
B ☐ £32
C ☐ £35
D ☐ £160

8. Use the data in question 7 to answer this question.

What is the range of the amounts of sponsorship money collected?

A ☐ £60
B ☐ £50
C ☐ £10
D ☐ £35

9. A man drove 386 miles over four days. The amounts of fuel he used each day are shown in the table. He wants to work out how much fuel he used each day, on average.

Day	Fuel (litres)
1	10
2	11
3	9
4	16

To do this, he needs to add the number of litres used and then:

A ☐ divide by 4
B ☐ multiply by 4
C ☐ divide by 386
D ☐ subtract from 386

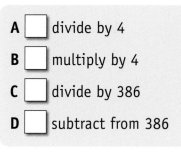

Published by:
Edexcel Limited
One90 High Holborn
London
WC1V 7BH
www.edexcel.org.uk

Distributed by:
Pearson Education Limited
Edinburgh Gate
Harlow
Essex
CM20 2JE

© Edexcel Limited 2006

All rights reserved. No part of this publication may be reproduced, stored in a retrieval system, or transmitted in any form or by any means, electronic, mechanic, photocopying, recording, or otherwise without either the prior permission of the Publishers or a licence permitting restricted copying in the United Kingdom issued by the Copyright Licensing Agency Ltd, 90 Tottenham Court Road, London W1P 9HE.

First published 2006
Third impression 2009

ISBN: 978-1-84690-135-5

Edited and typeset by Ken Vail Graphic Design
Illustrated by Ken Vail Graphic Design and Beehive Illustration (Mark Turner)
Cover and text design by Ken Vail Graphic Design
Cover image GettyImages/James Oliver
Printed and bound in China (SWTC/03)

The Publisher's policy is to use paper manufactured from sustainable forests.

Hot Topics CD
This CD was produced as part of the DfES Move On project 2003–6 and carries Crown copyright. Details of the Move On project and its successor Move On Up, commissioned by QIA, can be found at www.move-on.org.uk.